# The History Quiz Book - Part II

# The History Quiz Book

## PART II

## Judy Lloyd

THE HIGHBURY PRESS

First published in 1996 by

The Highbury Press
15 Monsell Road
London N4 2EF
Telephone: 0171–359 1933

A catalogue record for this book is available from the British Library

ISBN 0-9525655-1-X

Printed and bound in Great Britain by
Biddles Ltd, Guildford, Surrey

*This book is dedicated to my twin brother*

*Tom (né Thomas)*

*with all my love, admiration and*

*thanks for the £££s*

# *Author's Note*

I assume that most people who are reading Part II of *The History Quiz Book* will have already read Part I, so will not bore you by repeating the Preface.

If there seems to be a demand for Part III, I will attempt to publish it in 1997, but more likely in 1998.

Since humour is such an important element of these books, and my store of it is now thoroughly depleted, please send in to me any good historical anecdotes for inclusion in Part III.

I am sorry that I have had to put the price up, but publishing is much more expensive than I had anticipated.

London
August 1996

# Acknowledgements

I thank the following people for their help and encouragement: Me Mum, Alan Blease, James Escarelle-Rees, Gerald Hill, Nick Alexander, Eric Small, Melissa Blease, Nicholas and Ann Bagnall, Catherine Shakespeare Lane, Sir David Barber, Kenneth Rose, Lady Mansfield, Pete Gas, Harry Gates, Sandra Fordyce, Sylvia Hill, Eliot Edwards, Daphne Trotter, Helen Donlon and Helen Simpson.

The cover illustration from the Becket Leaves at the British Library is reproduced by kind permission of Sotheby's and J. Paul Getty KBE, Wormsley Library.

The Highbury Press logo of the brass rubbing of the figure of Sir Robert Wilson is reproduced by kind permission of the Westminster Abbey Brass Rubbing Centre.

# Mea Maxima Culpa

In Part I, I referred to Edmund Burke as one of the finest orators of all time (Quiz 44). Not necessarily. I have subsequently read that Burke was such an incredibly boring speaker that his fellow MPs tended to leave the chamber to take refreshment as soon as he got up to speak. He therefore became known, by friends and opponents alike, as 'the Dinner Bell'.

Thanks are due to my friend Hal Johnson of Nashville, Tennessee, for pointing out so forthrightly that Ulysses S. Grant did *not* succeed to the presidency after the assassination of Abraham Lincoln. It was, of course, Andrew Johnson, Lincoln's Vice-President (Quiz 24).

# Questions

# QUIZ 1

1. Who was dubbed 'Miss Canary Islands 1936' by his exasperated co-conspirators for his coy reluctance to commit himself to revolution while military governor of the islands?

2. When did the Pope become infallible?

3. The Archduchess Maria-Maddalena visited her son, the dissolute Grand Duke Ferdinando de' Medici, with a list of Florentine nobles involved in a particularly grotesque form of carnal abuse, demanding that they all be severely punished. What did Ferdinando do?

4. 'It was with a sense of awe that they turned upon Russia the most grisly of all weapons. They transported him in a sealed truck like a plague bacillus.' Who was Winston Churchill describing?

5. What was Abraham Lincoln's objective in fighting the American Civil War?

6. Who was murdered by Ingram Frizer during a tavern brawl at Deptford in 1593?

7. Which Swede collected and classified a wide range of plants, thus becoming the father of modern botany?

8. What was Disraeli's cruel comment when Joseph Biggar stood up to make his maiden speech in the House of Commons?

9. Which high-street travel business originated in a railway journey from Leicester to Loughborough to promote temperance, 150 years ago?

10. Which national newspaper was founded in Manchester in the aftermath of the Peterloo Massacre?

11. Who showed remarkable restraint at Fashoda in September 1898?

12. Who were the Adullamites?

13. Who said 'There's a sucker born every minute'?

14. Whose political career was destroyed by his affair with Mrs O'Shea?

1

1. Why did the presidential mansion built of Virginia sandstone become known as the White House?

2. John Wilkes, knowing how the Prince Regent hated his ailing father, George III, proposed a toast, saying, 'The King, long life to him.' 'Since when,' demanded the irritated Prince, 'have you been so anxious about my parent's health?' What was Wilkes's reply?

3. What was the Rye House Plot?

4. Which English king was effectively deposed at the Battle of Lewes in 1264?

5. When was Wales united with England?

6. What was the surprising first career of Charles XIV John, King of Sweden?

7. How is Empress Tz'u Hsi better known?

8. What instructions did Lord Curzon give his second wife, Grace, on the subject of making love?

9. Which English king imprisoned his elder brother, Robert of Normandy, in Cardiff Castle for twenty-eight years?

10. Who were Charles the Fat, Charles the Bald, Charles the Bold, Charles the Bad, Charles the Simple and Charles the Mad?

11. Which territory was ceded to Britain by the Treaty of Nanking (now Nanjing) in August 1842?

12. Which future prime minister led the cavalry charge of the 21st Lancers at the Battle of Omdurman in 1898?

13. What was Benjamin Disraeli's famous 'leap in the dark'?

14. From whom do we derive our word 'lynch'?

# QUIZ 3

1. Who died by falling down the stairs at Cumnor Place?

2. Which is the oldest parliament in the world?

3. Who said, 'For the first time I am ashamed to be German,' when he heard of Hitler's brutal treatment of the Jews just before the outbreak of World War II?

4. Which prime minister, aged sixty, had a passionate correspondence with Venetia Stanley, aged twenty-six, the daughter of his friend Lord Sheffield, between 1912 and 1915?

5. Which empress bought the two great libraries of the French Enlightenment (those of Voltaire and Diderot), Sir Robert Walpole's collection of paintings and three other major European art collections?

6. What was Benjamin Disraeli's response to the suggestion that he should use an extra-marital sex scandal to discredit the elderly but sprightly Lord Palmerston during an election campaign?

7. Which famous Italian painting did François I of France buy in 1517 to hang in his lavatory?

8. Why did hotels suddenly proliferate in New York in the mid-1890s?

9. Who was the land-agent who was ostracized by the Irish Land League for a series of ruthless tenant evictions in County Mayo in 1880?

10. Who to Machiavelli embodied the Prince in his book of that name?

11. Who watched Rome burn from the Tower of Maecenas, singing Homer's lines on the ruin of Troy and accompanying himself on the lyre?

12. Two of the greatest military geniuses of all time were born in the same year, 1769. Who were they?

13. Who was bled to death by his doctors at Missolonghi, Greece, in 1824?

14. Why is the tank called a tank and not an armoured fighting vehicle?

3

# QUIZ 4

1. 'I vow to God I don't know what I shall do with my awkward son . . . He has put on his red coat for the first time today. Anyone can see he has not the cut of a soldier.' The Countess of Mornington's disparaging comment on which future general?

2. Which famous uprising was led by Robert Aske?

3. Why did Erik the Red name Greenland Greenland – which it most definitely isn't?

4. How is the massacre of the occupying Angevin French by the natives of Palermo in 1282 better known?

5. How did Toba, the fifteen-year-old emperor of Japan, solve the succession problem on his accession to the throne in 1118?

6. What was known as the Porte or the Sublime Porte?

7. Whom did the Romans acknowledge as King of Britain in AD 5?

8. Who became known as 'the Father of the RAF'?

9. Which famous general was drowned on HMS *Hampshire* when it was sunk by a German mine off the Orkney Islands in 1915?

10. When the new MP Sir Alfred Bossom first entered the House of Commons, what did Winston Churchill mutter to a colleague?

11. Which emperor was shot by a firing squad of the Mexican Republican Army at Querétaro in 1867?

12. Who were the combatants at the Battle of Pharsalus in 48 BC?

13. Who suffered a disastrous defeat on the plain of Kosovo at the hands of the Ottoman Turks in 1389?

14. Who was assassinated during a performance of Rimsky-Korsakov's opera *Tsar Sultan* at Kiev in September 1911?

# QUIZ 5

1. '[A] deluded, excited man of eighty-two trying to govern England and her vast Empire with the miserable democrats under him is quite ludicrous . . . a bad joke.' Queen Victoria on which prime minister?

2. Which Ottoman sultan was exiled by the Young Turks in 1909 to Salonika, amid much rejoicing, with only three of his wives, four concubines, four eunuchs and fourteen servants?

3. Name the Kaiser's commander-in-chief during World War I.

4. Who was the first queen regnant (as opposed to queen consort) of England?

5. Why did General William Howe fail to follow up his victories at White Plains, Brandywine and Germantown by destroying Washington's army during the American War of Independence?

6. Why did toy bears become known as Teddy bears?

7. Which period of history became known as the Pax Britannica?

8. What were the Lumière brothers responsible for in Paris in 1895?

9. Which Venetian became a favourite of Kublai Khan, travelled widely in China and Central Asia and dictated his memoirs to a fellow prisoner in a Genoese jail?

10. What did Vincenzo Perugia steal from the Louvre in 1911?

11. In what year were the first Olympic Games held?

12. What was Louis XV's notorious Parc aux Cerfs?

13. How did King Louis-Philippe of France react to the news that Talleyrand, one of the most brilliant but devious statesmen of his age, had died?

14. How is the Earl of Chester, Duke of Rothesay, Earl of Carrick, Baron Renfrew, Lord of the Isles and Great Steward of Scotland better known?

5

1. During which naval battle did Admiral Beatty remark, 'There seems to be something wrong with our bloody ships today and our system'?

2. Who became known as 'the Black Napoleon'?

3. What is the origin of the phrase 'sent to Coventry'?

4. How is the Spanish patriot Rodrigo Díaz de Vivar better known?

5. What made Wellington unpopular among art-lovers in post-Waterloo occupied Paris?

6. Which continent was named after the daughter of Agenor, who in Greek legend was king of the Levantine city of Tyre?

7. Who is known as 'the Father of Medicine'?

8. What did Albrecht of Hohenzollern, Philip, Landgrave of Hesse, the Margrave of Brandenburg-Ansbach, the Dukes of Schleswig and Brunswick and the Count of Mansfield do between 1525 and 1528?

9. How was the Dutch-born Margaretha Gertruda MacLeod (née Zelle) better known?

10. What did F. E. Smith reply when Woodrow Wilson asked what in his opinion was the trend of the modern English undergraduate?

11. Who founded the Merovingian Empire in Gaul, defeated the Romans at Soissons in 486 and the Visigoths at Poitiers in 507, and made Paris his capital?

12. Who said, while contemplating his mirror image, 'Odd's fish, I am an ugly fellow'?

13. Roman history is divided into which two distinct epochs?

14. Whose widespread public support in the face of his expulsion from parliament and exile could be said to have founded English Radicalism?

# QUIZ 7

1. Who were the protesters who gave us the word 'Protestant'?

2. Which of Louis XV's mistresses was guillotined during the Reign of Terror?

3. Which English king was starved to death in Pontefract Castle?

4. 'All is lost. Monks, monks, monks.' Whose last words?

5. What did James II have in common with King Lear?

6. What was the subject of Eisenstein's film *The Battleship Potemkin*?

7. How did Robert Clive reply to a question from an MP about the extent of his corrupt activities as Governor of Bengal?

8. What was the significance of the Emperor Constantine's defeat of his rival Maxentius at the Milvian Bridge outside Rome in AD 312?

9. Whom did Alexander the Great defeat at the Battle of the River Granicus in Asia Minor in 334 BC?

10. After which battle in 1757 did Voltaire comment, 'German nationalism was born on that day'?

11. Who sacked Rome in 1527?

12. Which German emperor died of throat cancer after a reign of only ninety-nine days?

13. In 1985 a British Rail spokesman said, 'We have just refurbished platform 8, and anyone wanting to dig it up had better come up with a strong case.' Who may be buried under platform 8 at King's Cross?

14. What did Colonel John Jones (Cromwell's brother-in-law), Colonel Adrian Scroope, Colonel Thomas Harrison, John Carew, Thomas Scot, Gregory Clement, Colonel John Okey, Colonel John Barkstead and Colonel Miles Corbet have in common?

# QUIZ 8

1. What is the link between General Erwin von Witzleben, Carl Frederick Goerdeler, Colonel Hans Oster, General Ludwig Beck, Lieutenant-Colonel Klaus von Stauffenberg and many others?

2. Which two grandchildren of Charles I became joint rulers of Britain?

3. Why did the naturally chatty William the Silent become taciturn for seven years?

4. Who drowned in Starnberg Lake with Dr von Gudden in 1886?

5. 'What he saw in any of us I cannot tell. We were all plain, and if any of us had wit, he would not have understood it.' Which English king was Catherine Sedley talking about?

6. Why was AD 406 a turning-point in English history?

7. Which 25-year-old king marshalled an army of nearly 70,000 men in 1707 with the intention of invading Russia and marching on Moscow?

8. Which Dutch garrison town held out in 1701 against the army of Louis XIV, when Mons, Antwerp, Namur, Liège and other towns surrendered without firing a shot?

9. What did Pope Urban II proclaim in 1095 in Clermont, France?

10. Which ninth-century emperor held dominion over France (except Brittany), northern Italy and western Germany?

11. 'I pray God save the King, and send him long to reign over you, for a gentler and more merciful Prince was there never, and to me he was ever a good, a gentle and sovereign Lord.' Whose astonishingly forgiving words?

12. Which great monument of the Classical world was destroyed by the Venetian Admiral Francesco Morosini on 26 September 1687?

13. When did the Jewish Diaspora begin?

14. Who fought the battles of Lake Trasimene (217 BC) and Cannae (216 BC)?

# QUIZ 9

1. How did Clemens Metternich forfeit Austria's chances of acquiring Bavaria at the Congress of Vienna in 1815?

2. Who defeated Pompey at the momentous Battle of Pharsalus in 48 BC?

3. How was Louis XV related to Louis XIV?

4. Who said in 1862, 'The great questions of the day will be decided not by speeches and majority votes – that was the great mistake of 1848 and 1840 – but by iron and blood' [*Eisen und Blut*]?

5. What document, burnt in front of Queen Victoria by the Duke of Buccleuch as a declaration of loyalty to her, proved that he was the rightful king and would have given the present duke a claim to the throne?

6. Who finally overran Greece in 337 BC?

7. How did the exiled John Wilkes reply to Marie-Antoinette's question, 'How far can a man go in your country and not lose his head?'

8. Which war did Winston Churchill describe as 'the first World War'?

9. When was constitutional monarchy established in Britain?

10. 'The angel of death has been abroad throughout the land. You can hear the beating of its wings.' John Bright's bleak comment (made in February 1855) about which war?

11. What were Henry VIII's destructive invasions of Scotland in 1544 and 1545 nicknamed?

12. Who was the first female MP in Britain?

13. The years between 1629 and 1640 have been described conflictingly as those 'of the fullest calm and greatest felicity' and 'the Eleven Years' Tyranny'. What was significant about this decade?

14. Which royal duke, an uncle of Queen Victoria, was rumoured to have murdered his valet, Sellis, as a punishment for interrupting the duke while he was making love to Sellis's wife?

1. 'Home we bring our bold whoremonger,/Romans, lock your wives away!/All the bags of gold you sent him/Went his Gallic tarts to pay.' Which famous Roman was the subject of this contemporary rhyme?

2. When was London effectively under Dutch military occupation for a period of eighteen months?

3. John Dryden's epic, toadying poem 'Annus Mirabilis' celebrated which year in English history?

4. When was the last serious bout of Republicanism in Great Britain?

5. What was the subject of John Reed's famous book entitled *Ten Days that Shook the World*?

6. Which prime minister introduced the two (Irish) Home Rule Bills of 1886 and 1893?

7. What was the famous 'blank cheque' presented by Kaiser Wilhelm to Emperor Franz Josef in July 1914?

8. What is another name for the Eastern Roman Empire?

9. Who fathered two sons on the laundress Alexandrine Elenora Vergeot or La Belle Sabotière, while imprisoned in the fortress of Ham, in France?

10. When did Christianity first reach Britain?

11. Which pope is regarded as 'the father of the Roman Catholic Church'?

12. Who, in 1911, was the first man to reach the South Pole?

13. Who sacked Rome in AD 455, but on this occasion did not live up to their name?

14. Which Dominican friar drove the ruling Medici family out of Florence in 1497, with the help of Charles VIII of France, and set up a puritanical democratic republic?

# QUIZ 11

1. Which First Sea Lord kept his mistress, Martha Ray, at the Admiralty during the day 'so as to obtain occasional relief from the tedium of official business'?

2. When did Russia have two tsars ruling simultaneously?

3. What was the Ottonian Empire?

4. In the unlikely event that someone tells you to 'go to Canossa', what historical incident would they be referring to?

5. What was the Peace of Wedmore in AD 878?

6. How did Russia get its name?

7. Which two famous battles (during different wars) were fought on the mainland of Continental Europe in 1709?

8. 'I wished to found a European system, a European Code of Laws, a European judiciary: there would be but one people in Europe.' Who said it?

9. Who made himself extremely unpopular in England when he sent a telegram of congratulations to President Paul Kruger after his suppression of the Jameson Raid in January 1896?

10. Which empire lasted longer, the Roman or the Ottoman?

11. Which two words did prostitutes in Ancient Greece have carved on the soles of their shoes?

12. Who was the first English Christian martyr?

13. Who was crowned Holy Roman Emperor at Aix-la-Chapelle on 23 October 1519?

14. Who declared patriotism to be 'the last refuge of a scoundrel'?

11

# QUIZ 12

1. At the start of the Seven Years War, Frederick the Great of Prussia said, 'England has long been in labour, but at last she has brought forth a man.' Which future prime minister was he talking about?

2. When the papal legate, Cardinal Humbert, placed a bull of excommunication on the altar at Saint Sophia, Constantinople, in 1054 against Patriarch Michael Cerularius, why was it significant for Christendom?

3. What did John Stuart Mill's maid do with the only copy of Thomas Carlyle's manuscript of his great œuvre *The French Revolution*?

4. Who stunned all Europe by his lightning march from Holland to the Danube to join the Imperial Austro-Hungarian army defending Vienna?

5. What is Sir Robert Brackenbury, Constable of the Tower of London, reputed to have refused to do in 1483?

6. Where did the Royalists establish their headquarters in the Civil War?

7. Who was the first King of a united (ancient) Egypt?

8. Who committed suicide at Libyssa (northern Turkey) in 183 BC?

9. Sir John Burgogne was called a 'nincompoop', Sir George Brown 'the biggest fool in the army', General Bentinck 'the biggest fool ever'. Which war was fought by this unedifying phalanx of commanders?

10. Which peace treaty is said to have established Great Britain as a world imperial power?

11. Why did General Napier telegraph the Latin word *Peccavi* after his subjugation of Sind province in north-east India in 1843?

12. Who was New York named after?

13. Who identified/discovered X-rays in 1895?

14. Which English king was accused by a French newspaper of contracting a bigamous marriage, having already married the daughter of Admiral Sir Calne-Seymour?

12

# QUIZ 13

1. 'The mystic cords of memory, stretching from every battlefield and patriot grave to every living heart and hearth-stone all over this broad land, will yet swell the chorus of the Union.' Part of the peroration of which US president's inaugural speech?

2. Which famous man was born in c. 6 BC?

3. What were Britain's Local Defence Volunteers or LDV nicknamed?

4. Who was victorious at the important naval battles of Salamis in 480 BC and Mycale the following year?

5. Who said, with remarkable filial candour, 'My father was probably the greatest natural Don Juan in the history of British politics'?

6. Which is the oldest existing city in the world?

7. Which political philosopher was born at Trier, Germany, in 1818?

8. What did Joseph Priestley discover, in 1774, when he heated red mercuric oxide?

9. Which English king defeated the French at the naval battle of Sluys in 1340, virtually wiping out the French navy?

10. Who said to the Rump Parliament, 'You have sat too long here for any good you have been doing. Depart . . . In the name of God, go'?

11. Which country did the Roman Emperor Claudius annexe in AD 43?

12. Edmund Burke campaigned obsessively for fourteen years to disgrace which colonial administrator?

13. What did Robert Fulton demonstrate in Paris in 1797 as a weapon of war against the British?

14. Lord Holland, father of Charles James Fox, had an eccentric friend called George Selwyn, a notorious necrophiliac (he would travel for miles to watch public executions). When the ailing Holland heard that Selwyn had called to enquire about his health, what was his reply?

13

# QUIZ 14

1. Who was the last Queen of France?

2. How did Charles II's good friend Sir Charles Sedley embarrass his sovereign in Bow Street?

3. What was the significance of the defeat of the Byzantine army at the Battle of Manzikert, in Asia Minor, in August 1071?

4. Before the Reform Act of 1832 the constituencies of Old Sarum, in Wiltshire, and Old Dunwich, in Suffolk, both returned two MPs. Why were they in urgent need of reform?

5. 'There, my Lord! There is your enemy! There are your guns!' Who spoke these words and which military disaster did they herald?

6. Which famous American hero died during the defence of the Alamo in March 1836?

7. Who said, 'A fully equipped Duke costs as much to keep up as two dreadnoughts. They are just as great a terror, and they last longer'?

8. What did Howard Carter and Lord Carnarvon find in 1922?

9. Which English king carried off the Coronation stone or 'Stone of Destiny' from Scone in Scotland in 1296?

10. How old is the Bronze Age body found in the ice near Innsbruck in 1991?

11. Which Zulu king's military genius was said to rival that of Napoleon and Wellington?

12. Who was the first Englishman to circumnavigate the world?

13. What was Talleyrand's response to Tsar Alexander's criticism of the King of Saxony, at the Congress of Vienna, that he had 'betrayed the cause of Europe' by his continued support of Napoleon?

14. Who was the notorious third wife of the doltish Roman Emperor Claudius?

# QUIZ 15

1. In 1792 Goethe witnessed a battle west of Paris and observed, 'From this place and from this day forth commences a new era in the world's history, and you can all say that you were present.' Which battle?

2. Who tried to buy his freedom by promising the conquistador Pizarro to fill a room 22 feet long and 17 feet wide with gold objects?

3. Which invading army did the Romans (and the Visigoths, Franks and Burgundians) defeat at the battle of Châlons-sur-Marne in June 451?

4. Which dying French king said to his heir, 'Remain at peace with your neighbours. I loved war too much. Do not follow me in that or in overspending.'

5. Which two generals met for a parley near Zama (Tunisia) in 202 BC?

6. Which king has been much criticized for denying asylum to his cousin Tsar Nicholas II and his family?

7. Who was born Iosif Vissarionovich Dzhugashvili on 21 December 1879 at Gori, Georgia?

8. Which of Charles I's ministers was condemned to death for treason by a Bill of Attainder and executed on 12 May 1641?

9. What was the 'Lost Colony'?

10. Who abdicated at Uppsala Castle on 16 June 1654?

11. What happened to the (Western) Roman Empire in AD 476?

12. Whom did Lord Hervey describe as being 'as coquette as if she were eighteen, and as rampant as if she were drunk'?

13. Which head waiter, born a slave, became a king?

14. Which Roman emperor tried to kill his mother, Agrippina, by poison (three times), contrived to make the ceiling above her bed collapse, and when that failed built a 'coffin ship', which he had specially constructed to fall apart when she set sail?

15

1. What did the Byzantine Empress Irene, Ivan the Terrible, Süleyman the Magnificent, Philip II of Spain, Peter the Great and Constantine the Great have in common?

2. Whose crown, lodged in Vienna, did Hitler demand to have sent to him in Nuremberg?

3. Why did the Regency fop Prince Boothby commit suicide?

4. How was the Limerick-born dancer Eliza Gilbert better known? Her tarantella was so dire that she was booed off every stage in Europe.

5. Where was the Bayeux Tapestry sewn?

6. What was the first republic in Western Europe?

7. Which king of England was recognized as the heir to the throne of France by the Treaty of Troyes in 1420?

8. Which major nineteenth-century war was ostensibly caused by yet another dispute over the Spanish succession?

9. Who was executed at Fotheringay Castle on 8 February 1587?

10. Which English monarch declared, 'There is only one Jesus Christ and one faith: the rest is a dispute about trifles'?

11. What uncomfortable accident obsessed Alexandra, the aunt of Ludwig II of Bavaria?

12. What was Britain's first overseas colony?

13. The Battle of Gravelines was the climax of which conflict?

14. Who was assassinated at Delft on 10 July 1584 by Balthasar Gérards, a cabinet-maker's apprentice?

**QUIZ 17**

1. The Marquis of Spinola, Count Ernst von Mansfield, Albrecht von Wallenstein and Count Johann von Tilly were leading military commanders in which seventeenth-century war?

2. Who was the famous son of Pepin the Short?

3. Who founded the Women's Social and Political Union in 1903?

4. Who was assassinated by the fanatical Roman Catholic monk François Ravaillac in Paris on 14 May 1610?

5. How is the frontierswoman Martha Jane Burke better known?

6. Who allegedly said, 'My father was frightened of his mother. I was frightened of my father, and I'm damned well going to make sure that my children are frightened of me'?

7. Who was garrotted like a common criminal at Cajamarca in Peru in 1533, on trumped-up charges of plotting against the Spanish?

8. Who introduced tobacco to England?

9. What important event, which took place 2,500 years ago, did the Greeks celebrate with their Democracy Week in June 1993?

10. How many prime ministers did Great Britain have in 1827?

11. Who were the signatories of the important Treaty of Paris on 3 September 1783?

12. Who massacred three Roman legions (20,000 men) under Quinctilius Varus in AD 9 in the Teutoburg Forest in what is now Germany?

13. Which 84-year-old general ignored an order from his emperor to seek a truce, and soundly defeated the rebel army of King Charles Albert of Sardinia in July 1848, thus restoring Austrian rule to northern Italy?

14. What is the derivation of the word 'slave'?

1. What did Henry VIII, Charles I and George V have in common?

2. Whose troops, led by Coenus, mutinied at the Beas River in 326 BC?

3. How did the lecherous Philip, Landgrave of Hesse, a pillar of the Protestant establishment, delight the Roman Catholics in 1540?

4. Which king of England as a very young man was rumoured to have contracted a marriage to a beautiful Quaker girl, Hannah Lightfoot?

5. Which emperor died in exile in Madeira on 1 April 1922?

6. What was the Treaty of Tordesillas of 1494?

7. Which Roman emperor had his eldest son, Crispus, put to death, had his second wife, Fausta, drowned in a scalding bath, and killed his eleven-year-old nephew?

8. Who paid this graceful tribute to the Marquis de Lafayette on 4 July 1917: 'Here and now, in the presence of the illustrious dead, we pledge our hearts and our honour in carrying this war to a successful issue. Lafayette, we are here.'

9. How did Peter the Great offend the dignity of his hirsute boyars who greeted him upon his return from his embassy to the West?

10. Charles VII was crowned King of France at Reims in 1429. Who was crowned King of France at Notre Dame two years later?

11. Who sculpted the Elgin Marbles?

12. Which Central American civilization made around 30,000 human sacrifices every year to propitiate their gods?

13. Who were the first Iconoclasts?

14. 'Two acres of cheeks spread with crimson, an ocean of red that overflowed and was not distinguished from the lower parts of the body and no part restrained by stays.' Horace Walpole on which of George I's mistresses?

# QUIZ 19

1.  Which English queen died of smallpox at the age of thirty-two?

2.  Who first demonstrated electric telegraphy by sending a message from Washington to Baltimore in 1844?

3.  Who died in Nebuchadnezzar's palace at Babylon on 10 June 323 BC from a malarial fever, probably aggravated by alcohol consumption, after attending a party thrown by his friend Medius?

4.  Who confided to a friend, 'The Duke returned from the war today and did pleasure me in his top boots'?

5.  How many emperors ruled Rome in AD 69?

6.  Who was born at Domrémy in the Duchy of Lorraine on 6 January 1412?

7.  Where did Nelson lose his right arm?

8.  Who in 175 BC reiterated the chilling command 'Delenda est Carthago' ('Carthage must be destroyed') in every speech he gave to the Roman Senate?

9.  Which country became part of Great Britain in 1801?

10. Which famous poet was appointed Latin Secretary to Oliver Cromwell's Council of State in 1651?

11. Which British business weekly magazine was founded by James Wilson in 1843 to promote free trade during the parliamentary conflict over the repeal of the Corn Laws?

12. What was Prime Minister Asquith doing on a Monday morning when Andrew Bonar Law had to consult him on a political crisis in 1916? It was just five days after the momentous Battle of Jutland.

13. Who was responsible for the death of up to 40,000,000 people in north and central China between 1643 and 1647?

14. Which dynasty ruled France from 987 to 1328?

19

1. How did Prime Minister Stanley Baldwin hit back when the *Daily Mail* commented that 'it is difficult to know how the leader of a party who had lost his own fortune can hope to restore anyone else's, or those of his country'?

2. Which European country, according to John Buchan, attempted four different forms of government in the seventeenth century: military dictatorship; dictatorship with a non-elected parliament; dictatorship with a written instrument; and a quasi-constitutional monarchy?

3. Which famous Lord Mayor of London helped finance Henry V's war with France (the Hundred Years War)?

4. What is the derivation of the word 'mausoleum'?

5. Who was the famous father of Ögödei?

6. Which medieval emperor was known as 'Stupor Mundi' or 'Wonder of the World'?

7. Who said upon their accession to the throne, 'Oh God, guide us, protect us, for we are too young to rule'?

8. Who was the famous pupil of Erik Jan Hanussen, a tutor in the arts of mass psychology, elocution and the use of body language?

9. Who invented the valve-and-siphon flush lavatory in about 1878?

10. Who, according to a vicious contemporary wit, 'gave up his position as Admiral of the Fleet . . . to be a third mate of a Baltimore tramp'?

11. What did Jeanne de Luxembourg sell the English for £800,00 in 1430?

12. Who was the first Labour prime minister?

13. Which English hero did James I execute in 1618 in an attempt to placate the Spanish ambassador, Señor Gondomar?

14. Who led the March of the Ten Thousand from Babylon to the Black Sea in 401 BC?

# QUIZ 21

1. What was the Duke of Devonshire's response when he heard of Stanley Baldwin's attack on the press barons (see Quiz 20)?

2. To whom did the dying Edward VI bequeath his throne in 1553?

3. What did Captain John Alcock and Lieutenant Arthur Whitten Brown do in June 1919?

4. Why did Oliver Cromwell's eleven major-generals become so unpopular from 1655?

5. Which French revolutionary leader said before his execution by guillotine, 'Show my head to the people. It's worth it'?

6. Who defeated a large elite force of Teutonic Knights and Knights Templar at Liegnitz in April 1241, slaughtering some 30,000 of them?

7. Which conflict was, according to the French statesman Adolphe Thiers, 'a war to give a few wretched monks the key of a grotto'?

8. On what charge was Clarence Darrow employed to defend the Tennessee biology teacher John Scopes in July 1925?

9. Whom did the naval lieutenant John Felton assassinate in 1628?

10. When the more refined citizens of Gumbinnen wanted to rename their local river, the Pissa, they petitioned King Frederick William IV. How did he reply?

11. Who were the combatants at the Battle of the Dunes in June 1658?

12. 'It was weary work that sitting, with my hand in his in the night watches, trying to guide that mighty mind, as a child's had to be led – that trying to be cheerful, when I could scarcely help weeping.' Lord Rowton on the death of which prime minister in April 1881?

13. Which two titans clashed in high office in India from 1902 to 1905?

14. The execution by hanging in 1826 of the pious schoolmaster Cavetano Ripoli for heresy marked the demise of which infamous organization?

21

1. Who was strangled, then burnt at the stake, in October 1536 at Vilvorde near Brussels for translating the New Testament into English?

2. 'Five hundred men, chosen accidentally from among the unemployed.' What was Lloyd George describing?

3. Which cardinal resigned his Great Seal of Office after Cardinal Campeggio adjourned the Legantine Court which was adjudicating on the annulment of Henry VIII's marriage to Catherine of Aragon?

4. To which famous London landmark did Benjamin Hall give his name?

5. What was Margot Asquith's crushing riposte to Jean Harlow when Harlow pronounced the 't' in Margot at their introduction?

6. Who was the famous royal Stuart husband of Louise of Stolberg?

7. Who burnt his boats by beaching his boats at Villa Rica on the coast of Yucatán in February 1521?

8. Who lost the premiership to Stanley Baldwin after the resignation of Andrew Bonar Law?

9. What did the great architect Sir Edwin Lutyens say of a dubious piece of fish while lunching at a smart London restaurant?

10. Which famous letter was forged at 117 Eisenacherstrasse, Berlin, in September 1924?

11. What was the other major eleventh-century Norman conquest?

12. Which French marshal is said to have died of 'une surfeit de femmes' in 1750?

13. Who disguised himself as Jane Lane's servant to escape the attention of a troop of Roundheads on a journey to Abbot's Leigh?

14. Whose dispatches to *The Times* from the Crimean War alerted the public and the government to the deplorable conditions of the British troops?

# QUIZ 23

1. 'This vice brings in one hundred million francs in taxes every year. I will certainly forbid it at once – as soon as you can name a virtue that brings in as much revenue.' What was Napoleon III talking about?

2. Who were the combatants at the Battle of Quiberon Bay in November 1759?

3. Which French king became a saint?

4. Which empire dominated Cambodia and Laos between the ninth century and the fifteenth?

5. How did the *grande horizontale* Harriette Wilson reply to the Prince Regent's suggestion that she should pay him a visit?

6. During which war did the term 'fifth column' come into being?

7. Who was appointed Public Prosecutor to the Paris Committee of Public Safety in March 1793?

8. Who sailed up the Medway estuary in June 1667, sank or burnt four ships of the line and towed away the *Prince Charles*, pride of the British fleet, which was anchored at Chatham dockyards?

9. Who founded La Giovine Italia (the Young Italy movement) in 1831?

10. Who denounced the government of his own Conservative Party as 'an organised hypocrisy'?

11. Which unhappy trio of women once travelled in the same coach together to accompany Louis XIV to the front on one of his campaigns in the Netherlands?

12. How old was William Gladstone when he became prime minister for the fourth time?

13. Who was Linus's famous predecessor?

14. Who was the last king of the united kingdom of Israel?

# QUIZ 24

1. Which Prime Minister did John Maynard Keynes describe as 'This syren, this goat-footed bard, this half-human visitor to our age from the hag-ridden magic and enchanted woods of Celtic antiquity'?

2. Who led the Spartacist movement, in Germany, which demanded the formation of a true Socialist republic?

3. Why was Franklin D. Roosevelt's promise to repeal the Volstead Act during his electoral campaign of 1933 particularly popular?

4. What did French chemist Hippolyte Mège-Mouriés patent in 1869?

5. Who said, 'I would rather die a thousand times,' when invited to discuss surrender terms at Appomattox at the end of the American Civil War?

6. Where were the Carlist Wars fought?

7. Who led the short-lived Hungarian Revolution of 1848–9?

8. In 1778, what did Pitt the Elder say when he heard that the Duke of Richmond was to press for a motion to grant America independence?

9. Who wrote and published the magazine *The North Briton*, which made scurrilous allegations against George III, his ministers in general and Lord Bute in particular?

10. Who accused Pope Leo X of being 'no better than any other stinking sinner'?

11. Which ruler of one of the ancient world's largest empires was stabbed by his courtiers while fleeing Alexander the Great in an ox-cart?

12. Which future prime minister wrote that he enjoyed 'being made much of by a man who was daily decapitating half the province'?

13. Which Italian patriot worked as a candlemaker on Staten Island, New York, in 1850?

14. Which former British diplomat was captured by British soldiers as he landed from a German submarine at Tralee, County Kerry?

# QUIZ 25

1. Commandant le Comte Marie-Charles Esterhazy was the real culprit in which notorious miscarriage of justice?

2. Which emperor's sarcophagus lies in the crypt of the Benedictine monastery at Farnborough in Hampshire?

3. When asked his opinion of Lord John Russell, the distinguished reformist Prime Minister, what did Disraeli reply?

4. Who were the subjects of John Dryden's famous satirical poem *Absalom and Achitophel*, a masterpiece of anti-Whig propaganda?

5. King Mongkut was the inspiration behind which musical?

6. What did Dr Canon Godin of Maastricht sell to the French Marshal Pichegru for 600 bottles of wine in 1795?

7. What is a ziggurat?

8. Which two sages of the ancient oriental world died within a few years of each other?

9. Who, according to Margot Asquith, 'would kill his own mother just so that he could use her skin to make a drum to beat his own praises'?

10. Which future Prime Minister, while holidaying in Naples, revealed in a letter to Lord Aberdeen the horrifying prison conditions of the Neapolitan dissidents incarcerated after the 1848 Revolution?

11. What was Russia's 'small victorious war', cynically calculated by Vyacheslav Pleve 'to stem the tide of revolution' in 1905?

12. What did French foreign minister Aristide Briand and his American counterpart, Frank B. Kellogg, set out to achieve in August 1927?

13. Which anatomically named battle marked the end of the (American) Indian Wars?

14. What came into effect on the eleventh hour of the eleventh day of the eleventh month?

25

1. On what occasion did King Leopold II of the Belgians, Prince Nicholas I of Montenegro, Prince Albert of Monaco, Grand Duke Nicholas of Russia and Edward Prince of Wales foregather in 1898?

2. Before which World War II battle did Marshal Pétain make his famous declamation, 'Ils ne passeront pas'?

3. Who designed the jet engine?

4. Who calculated the value of *pi* in 225 BC?

5. Who led the 300-mile 'Salt March' from an ashram near Ahmedabad to Dandi in 1930, in defiance of the Salt Tax imposed by the British Raj?

6. What did Holy Roman Emperor Charles V reply when asked which language he spoke in his vast, polyglot empire?

7. Who was the first president of the Turkish Republic?

8. The Union of Kalmar in 1397 united which three European countries?

9. Who said, 'Be of good comfort, Master Ridley, and play the man. We shall this day light such a candle in England as by the Grace of God shall never be put out'?

10. Who founded the Persian Empire?

11. Who was known as 'the Winter Queen'?

12. Who was Britain's only illegitimate prime minister?

13. Who was the seventeenth Earl of Derby talking about when he admitted ruefully one day, 'He makes one feel so terribly plebeian'?

14. Who did Prince Felix Yusupov, Vladimir Purishkevich and Grand Duke Dmitry Pavlovich murder on 30 December 1916?

**QUIZ 27**

1. What, according to 'La Belle' Otero, was 'an experience every woman should enjoy'?

2. Who led the heroic seventeen-month revolt of the Venetians against the Austrians in 1848–9?

3. What caused share prices to fall 20 points on the Berlin Stock Exchange on 15 September 1930?

4. Which two high-ranking British ministers were forced to resign at the outbreak of World War I because of supposed German sympathies?

5. Which long march did Piet Retief and Andreas Pretorius lead in 1837?

6. Which English explorer was killed in Hawaii in February 1779?

7. What was Talleyrand's sanguine response when King Charles X of France bemoaned the fact that 'There is no middle course between the throne and the scaffold'?

8. Which party or faction ruled China from 1928 to 1949?

9. What did the Duc de Richelieu's chef invent from very limited ingredients when his ship was stormbound off Mahon, Minorca, before the Duc's capture of the port from the British in 1756?

10. 'Absolutism tempered by assassination': what was the Hanoverian statesman Ernst Münster describing in 1830?

11. Which epistolary novelist joined the household of Louis-Philippe, Duc d'Orléans in 1788 to foment revolution at the Palais-Royal?

12. Who was proclaimed 'Chief of the Spanish State' on 1 October 1936?

13. Who said, 'You can fool all the people some of the time, and some of the people all the time, but you can not fool all the people all of the time'?

14. The Battle of Sinope, in which a Russian naval squadron destroyed an Ottoman fleet in the Black Sea, was the prelude to which major war?

27

1. Which prime minister wrote the political novels *Coningsby*, *Sybil*, *Tancred*, *Lothair* and *Endymion*?

2. What did the American inventor Clarence Birdseye (1886–1956) pioneer while working in the fur trade?

3. Whom did Marshal Ney vow to 'bring back to Paris in an iron cage'?

4. Countess Ada Lovelace should share a great deal of Charles Babbage's glory for the invention of the computer. Who was her famous father?

5. Who was the first Protestant Archbishop of Canterbury?

6. How is the eleventh-century High King of Scotland, Mormaer of Moray, husband of the gentle Gruoch, more widely known?

7. What was the very taciturn President Calvin Coolidge's response to the taunt 'I've made a bet with a friend that I can get you to say at least three words this evening'?

8. Who fled France aboard *L'Express* disguised as Mr and Mrs William Smith with the help of Mr Jones, Her Britannic Majesty's vice-consul at Le Havre?

9. How did John Wilkes attempt to secure an election victory at Berwick-upon-Tweed in 1754?

10. How is the German Princess Sophie von Anhalt-Zerbst better known?

11. 'The wench had not an ounce of modesty . . . she unhesitatingly complied with the most shameless demand . . . and she would throw off her clothes and expose to all comers those parts . . . [which] should rightly remain hidden.' Who was the historian Procopius describing?

12. Who was Louis XIV's great military engineer?

13. Which Irishman prophesied, 'I may have signed my own death warrant,' when he signed the Anglo-Irish treaty in 1921?

14. Which war ended with the Peace of Vereeniging on 21 May 1902?

# QUIZ 29

1.  Whom did Louis XIV charge with the arrest of Nicolas Fouquet, his overweening and corrupt Superintendent of Finance?

2.  Why was Lord Charles Beresford discomfited when, during a weekend houseparty, he crept into his latest mistress's bedroom and with an exuberant cry of 'Cock-a-doodle doo!' leapt on to her bed?

3.  Orso Ipato and Ludovico Manin were the first and the last in a long line of what?

4.  The Duc de Choiseul-Praslin's murder of his neurotic wife and subsequent suicide contributed to the overthrow of which French king?

5.  Who was Anita Riberas's husband, with whom she eloped in Brazil?

6.  Which American rocket-launcher derived its name from its similarity to a sound contraption invented by comedian Bob Burns in the 1930s?

7.  How did Sir Henry Wotton describe the role of an ambassador?

8.  Where was the world's first steam-locomotive public railway?

9.  Who was given joint command in 1863 of the 'Ever Victorious Army', a ramshackle group of mercenaries formed in Shanghai to defeat the Taiping rebels?

10. Who, with the help of Lord George Bentinck, destroyed the leader of his own party, Sir Robert Peel, because of his U-turn over the repeal of the Corn Laws?

11. What did Dorothy Parker say when she heard that President Calvin Coolidge had died?

12. How did the atheist MP Charles Bradlaugh change the rules of parliament in 1888?

13. Who edited the *British Gazette*, the newspaper published by the government during the 1926 General Strike?

14. What did the Anti-Combination Acts of 1799 and 1800 proscribe?

1. 'We did not conceive it possible that even he would produce a paper so slipshod, so loose-jointed, so puerile, not alone in literary construction but in its ideas, its grasp . . . By the side of it mediocrity is superb.' The *Chicago Times*'s comment on which famous speech?

2. Which independence movement was initiated at the monastery of Agia Lavra on 25 March 1821?

3. Who first used a pendulum to demonstrate the earth's rotation, and invented the gyroscope in 1851?

4. The shelling of Fort Sumter was the first action in which war?

5. How many Crusades were there?

6. What was Winston Churchill's famous dismissal of naval tradition?

7. What word did the American investigative journalists Ira M. Tarbell, Lincoln Steffens and Upton Sinclair give to the English language?

8. Friedrich Ebert became president of which republic in February 1919?

9. How did the aviator Orville Wright like to explain the principle of aerodynamics?

10. Who was the famous son-in-law of Abu Bakr?

11. Which philosopher/economist became known as the 'Apostle of the 1688 [Glorious] Revolution'?

12. Who jousted for chestnuts in one of the most scandalous incidents in the history of the Renaissance papacy?

13. Which Communist leader did Stalin expel after a power struggle in 1929?

14. Who were the combatants at the naval Battle of Lepanto in October 1571?

# QUIZ 31

1. Who opened the Suez Canal in 1869?

2. Which was the last pitched battle to be fought wholly under sail in wooden sailing-ships?

3. Which leading French revolutionary was arrested for debt, abduction and adultery, and spent nearly four years in Vincennes prison?

4. What was the disquieting news, in August 1845, from a market-garden on the Isle of Wight that would become a harbinger of doom for a million and a half Irish people?

5. It was thought at one time that Randolph Churchill might have lung cancer, but tissue removed in a biopsy proved to be benign. What was Evelyn Waugh's comment on the news?

6. What did George V pledge to give up at the beginning of World War I?

7. Who commanded the British troops during the Boer War?

8. Which poet died on the island of Skyros on 23 April 1915, while *en route* to the Dardanelles, of blood-poisoning from a mosquito bite?

9. How did US Congressman John McGroarty answer a constituent worried about the deforestation of the Sierra Madre mountains?

10. Who gained an international reputation for exposing the cruel exploitation of native labour by European traders in the Congo and Peru?

11. Which ship, *en route* to Genoa from Boston, disappeared in mid-Atlantic in 1872 and was found abandoned four weeks later?

12. What was significant about the tenth-century Bishop Theodred's will?

13. Who searched for Richard I across Europe and finally found him imprisoned in a fortress by Leopold V, Duke of Austria?

14. The Duke of Nemours, Prince Leopold of Saxe-Coburg, Prince Paul of Württemberg, the Duke of Sussex, Prince Frederick of Orange and Prince Otto of Bavaria were all contenders for which throne?

1. What did the Sykes–Picot Agreement carve up in 1916–17?

2. Who was appointed Dictator of the Two Sicilies at Marsala in 1860?

3. How did the Declaration of Pillnitz of August 1791 threaten the French Revolution?

4. 'One could not even dignify him with the name of stuffed shirt. He was simply a hole in the air.' George Orwell on which prime minister?

5. What did the Polish-born Dr Ludwik invent in an attempt to overcome the language barriers of his Lithuanian-, Latvian-, Estonian-, German- and Russian-speaking compatriots?

6. The Battle of Hampton Roads was the first naval action of which war?

7. Who said, 'America is the only country which miraculously has gone from barbarism to decadence without the usual interval of civilisation'?

8. Who was the last Romanov Tsar?

9. Whose table-top harangue and call to arms at the Palais-Royal in Paris launched the insurrection that culminated in the Fall of the Bastille?

10. What did Nathaniel Canopus (a Cretan) introduce to England in 1641?

11. Whose 'thin red line' halted the Russian cavalry charge at the Battle of Balaclava?

12. What was F. E. Smith's often-quoted reply when an irate judge lashed out at him at the end of a long courtroom wrangle: 'What do you suppose I am on the bench for, Mr Smith?'

13. Who, in 538 BC, brought the first Babylonian Captivity to an end by freeing the Jews after their fifty years of exile?

14. How did Léon Gambetta, French Minister of the Interior, escape from Paris at the beginning of the Siege of Paris in October 1870?

# QUIZ 33

1. What territory was 'beyond the Pale' for safety-conscious English people during the medieval era?

2. Tiglath-Pileser III, Sargon II, Sennacherib and Ashurbanipal were rulers of which ancient empire?

3. How long did the Hundred Years War actually last?

4. How did King Dom Luis III of Portugal tragically break a record?

5. Who was the chief conspirator in the Gunpowder Plot?

6. At the outbreak of the American Civil War, he was working in his father's Illinois leather store, after an unsuccessful career in farming and real estate. Which famous American general?

7. 'His temper, naturally morose, has become licentiously peevish. Crossed by his Cabinet, he insults the House of Lords, and plagues the most eminent of his colleagues with the crabbed malice of a maundering witch.' Which prime minister was Disraeli insulting?

8. Who was brought back from retirement to replace Prince Louis of Battenberg as First Sea Lord in October 1914?

9. Which American president used to joke that he had slept through most of his term of office?

10. Which famous French writer returned in triumph from nearly twenty years' exile in September 1870 on the eve of the Siege of Paris?

11. Who ambushed whom at the Pass of Roncesvalles in the Pyrenees in AD 778, inflicting one of the most famous defeats in history?

12. Who led the coup of September 1923 in Spain and set up a military dictatorship (with the connivance of King Alfsonso XIII)?

13. What did Rowland Hill found in 1840?

14. Which German World War I field marshal collaborated with Hitler in the unsuccessful Munich Beer Hall Putsch of 1923?

1. Who defeated Vercingetorix, the High Chief of all Gaul, at Alesia (Mont Auxois), France, in 52 BC?

2. Which late-nineteenth-century war was ostensibly caused by another dispute over the Spanish Succession?

3. What was Clemenceau's comment on Woodrow Wilson's Fourteen Points (aimed at making the world safer for democracy)?

4. Which dying king was given a lethal dose of morphine 'to determine the end' by his doctor, Lord Dawson, to ensure that the news of the king's death would receive 'its first announcement in the morning papers rather than the less appropriate field of the evening journals'?

5. Who was the last English Roman Catholic monarch?

6. Who died a raving lunatic at Dragsholm fortress, Denmark, in 1578 after eleven years of cruel captivity?

7. Lord Halifax was in a train with three prim middle-aged matrons. As they were going through a tunnel he covered his hand with several wet noisy kisses. What did he say when they emerged from the tunnel?

8. How is 'Bonnie Dundee' better known?

9. Who coined the phrase 'England is the mother of Parliaments'?

10. How did the outrageous courtesan Ninon de Lenclos pass the time when she was banished to a monastery by Louis XIV's mother?

11. Who said, at the trial of Louis XVI, 'concerned to do my duty and convinced that all those who have conspired or will in future conspire against the sovereignty of the people deserve death, I vote for death'?

12. Which late-eighteenth-century mutiny is sometimes referred to as 'the Floating Republic'?

13. Which was the bloodiest battle fought on British soil?

14. Who made the first Atlantic crossing entirely under steam?

# QUIZ 35

1.  What was the *Reconquista*, which took place intermittently between AD 718 and 1492?

2.  Which prince was suspected of being involved in the notorious Cleveland Street male prostitute scandal?

3.  Which Russian writer was condemned to death in 1849 for his participation in the radical 'Petrashevsky Circle'?

4.  Whose modesty 'amounted to a deformity', according to Margot Asquith?

5.  Why did Islam fail to inspire Vladimir, Grand Prince of Kiev, when he was looking for a state religion to unite his feuding cities?

6.  Who declared that 'When a man assumes a public trust, he should consider himself public property'?

7.  How did the 960 Jewish Zealots escape capture and certain enslavement by the Romans in AD 73?

8.  He was 'great in the resources of a misguided mind, great in the conception and execution of evil. Awful indeed will be the sentence of history.' Chateaubriand on which famous Frenchman?

9.  How did 20,000 women and children die in southern Africa between 1899 and 1902?

10. When was the term 'Whig' first used in British politics?

11. Which powerful city-state was founded in the early fifth century by citizens of north-east Italy fleeing the depredations of the Goths?

12. How did the Earl of Jersey respond to the suggestion that he should fight duels in defence of his beautiful but unfaithful wife's honour?

13. What word did Governor Elbridge Gerry give to the English language?

14. Who abdicated at Olmutz, Moravia, in December 1848?

# QUIZ 36

1. What is the link between the American debutante Mary Phelps Jacobs and the Parisian couturier Madame Cadolle?

2. Who, armed with secret knowledge of the British victory at Waterloo, went to the Stock Exchange looking so gloomy that stocks fell, bought low, and made a killing by selling high after the victory was announced?

3. Who was born at Parsonage House, Burnham Thorpe, on 29 September 1785?

4. Which British head of state was reluctant to leave the confines of his palace at Whitehall in case he should be arrested for debt?

5. 'When he launched his scheme for peopling Palestine with Jewish immigrants, I am credibly informed that he didn't know there were any Arabs in the country.' Whom was Dean Inge maligning?

6. Who was responsible for the major reforms in the British army between 1868 and 1874?

7. Which Viceroy of India did Churchill nickname 'the Holy Fox'?

8. Who abdicated at the Hall of the Golden Fleece, Brussels, on 25 October 1556?

9. What disaster did the American economist Roger W. Babson predict in a speech to his Annual National Business Conference?

10. Sir Henry Havelock, Sir Colin Campbell and Sir Robert Napier were the heroes of which siege?

11. Why was Caligula's threat to promote Incitatus to consul considered extraordinary, even for him?

12. Who were massacred at Blood River in Natal on 16 December 1838?

13. Which former prime minister 'died as he lived, at sea'?

14. Whose death may have been hastened by prolonged exposure to toxic fumes from wallpaper permeated with a pigment containing arsenic?

# QUIZ 37

1. Who is often referred to as 'the Father of Railways'?

2. Which ancient conflict may have been fought to resolve disputes over trading rights in the Aegean (and control of the Dardenelles)?

3. In 1918 Tomáš Masaryk became the first president of which Eastern European country?

4. In a desperate plea for peace, which former foreign secretary wrote to the *Daily Telegraph* in 1917, saying, 'What will be the value of the blessings of peace to nations so exhausted that they can scarcely stretch out an arm with which to grasp them?'

5. How was Aircraftsman Shaw better known?

6. According to Aneurin 'Nye' Bevan, what were the two most effective methods of attaining high office?

7. Which famous legend did American clergyman Mason Locke Weems concoct?

8. What was the fateful birthday present that Foreign Minister Julius Andrassy presented to the Emperor Franz Josef in 1879?

9. Who is sometimes known as 'the last English King of England'?

10. How did the Labour MP Jack Jones respond to Lady Astor's vigorous pro-temperance assertion that she would rather commit adultery than drink a pint of beer?

11. Which empire's downfall is thought to have been partially caused by lead poisoning?

12. What did the Chinese eunuch Ts'ai Lun discover in AD 105?

13. Which leading French revolutionary acted as a secret adviser to Louis XVI and Marie-Antoinette from 1790?

14. What was the significance of the Battle of Ayn Jalut, near Jerusalem, in September 1260?

1. 'You are history. You are legend . . . and when the olive tree of peace puts forth its leaves again, mingled with the laurels of the Spanish republic's victory – come back!' La Pasionara's farewell to whom?

2. Which Dean of New College, Oxford, proposed a toast to Queen Victoria with the words 'Let us drink to the queer old Dean'?

3. To office in which organization did Pope Gregory IX appoint the Dominican friars Peter Seila and William Arnald in July 1233?

4. Which London street is named after a Scout Master General of Oliver Cromwell's army in Scotland?

5. Which English hero may have spoken the Turkish word *kismet* ('destiny') on his deathbed?

6. Who pleaded for the life of Captain John Smith at Chesapeake Bay as he laid his head on the sacrificial stone of the Powhatan tribe?

7. What was the sobriquet of Anna Protasova, Catherine the Great's lady-in-waiting and confidante?

8. What happened to time on 6 July 1189?

9. Whose reputation has suffered down the centuries because of a mistranslation of the word *grozny*?

10. Which of Louis XIV's mistresses was implicated in the 'Affair of the Poisons' which scandalized Paris in 1679?

11. Which word did Elizabeth I's physician, scientist William Gilbert, coin?

12. Which Roman emperor fell in love with the beautiful youth Sporus, had him castrated, went through a marriage ceremony (with all the trimmings) and lived with him in wedded bliss?

13. Who recruited and led the Indian Ambulance Corps in the Boer War?

14. What did the sixteenth-century historian Cardinal Baronius describe as 'the Pornocracy' (or 'the Reign of Harlots')?

# QUIZ 39

1. Which American land purchase became known as 'Seward's Folly'?

2. Which Spanish writer lost a hand at the Battle of Lepanto in 1571?

3. Who was Peeping Tom peeping at?

4. 'He is so vain that he wants to figure in history as the settler of all the great questions . . . His smile is like the silver fittings on a coffin.' Disraeli on which prime minister?

5. Which Albanian army officer, who began his career selling tobacco in a Thracian village, laid the foundations of the modern Egyptian state?

6. Whose name was mud in the immediate aftermath of Abraham Lincoln's assassination by John Wilkes-Booth?

7. What happened to Mustafa Kemal (Atatürk) in Damascus which made him turn his face from Islam?

8. The Harleian Miscellany is known to bibliophiles as one of the most valuable collection of prints and books in the British Library. What is the lesser-known and less reputable Harleian Miscellany?

9. Who were the combatants at the Battle of Plassey in June 1757?

10. Who floated the ill-fated 'Hawarden kite' on 17 December 1885?

11. Which British World War I campaign aimed to open the Dardenelles, take Istanbul, neutralize Turkey and ship supplies to the Russians?

12. What was the 1905 Relugas Compact?

13. How did William Randolph Hearst, editor and publisher of the *New York Journal*, reply to his correspondent Frederic Remington's cable from Cuba which said, 'Everything is quiet. There is no trouble here. There will be no war. I wish to return'?

14. What was the Kaiser studying when he wrote in the margin, 'It contains the announcement *orbi et urbi* of a capitulation of the most humiliating kind and with it every reason for war is removed'?

1. Why did the people of Rome chorus in relief 'Deo Gratias' ('Thanks be to God') when they heard 'Habet' ('He has') at the enthronement of each pope from the tenth century to the beginning of the sixteenth?

2. Which French revolutionary became known as 'Le Mitrailleur de Lyon' ('The Cannoneer of Lyon')?

3. Who declared prophetically that 'the broad mass of a nation . . . will more easily fall victim to a big lie than to a small one'?

4. Which national newspaper was founded in 1855 by Colonel Arthur Sleigh in order to pursue his vendetta against the Duke of Cambridge?

5. Which famous economist and philosopher lived at 28 Dean Street, 9 Grafton Terrace and 41 Maitland Park Road, London?

6. If 'coming out for cannibalism would get him . . . votes . . . he would begin fattening a missionary in the White House backyard come Wednesday.' H. L. Mencken on which US president's opportunism?

7. Who were the subjects of John Tenniel's famous *Punch* cartoon entitled 'Dropping the Pilot'?

8. Why did an ailing and furious Lenin demand an apology from Stalin in December 1922?

9. Which future prime minister resigned the leadership of his party over their decision to support war credits on 5 August 1914?

10. What was the nickname of the 11th Hussars while under Lord Cardigan's command from 1840?

11. Who discovered the neutron (a new sub-atomic particle) in 1932?

12. Which naval slang word derives from Admiral Vernon's nickname ?

13. Which cardinal led French troops to besiege the impregnable Huguenot stronghold of La Rochelle in 1627?

14. Who was the original Scott of the exclamation 'Great Scott'?

# QUIZ 41

1. Who was Alice Roosevelt Longworth referring to when she lamented, 'I do wish he did not look as if he had been weaned on pickle'?

2. Who made 'homespun' the potent symbol of a great nationalist movement in an economy severely damaged by imported cloth?

3. What was the link between the tenth-century popes John XII and Benedict VII?

4. At the start of the Spanish Civil War, which party was in power?

5. Who led the radical Montagnards during the French Revolution?

6. Which legendary English hero's exploits were probably based on those of a real-life follower of Simon de Montfort who was outlawed after de Montfort's defeat and death at the Battle of Evesham in 1265?

7. What did Fouché say when he heard that his arch-enemy Talleyrand had been made Vice-Grand Elector of the Empire by Napoleon?

8. Who was beheaded at Ioannina in 1822, after his ill-fated attempt to carve out an independent kingdom within the Ottoman Empire?

9. When a French journalist attacked Atatürk's autocratic rule by commenting that Turkey was governed by a drunkard, a deaf man (İsmet İnönü) and 300 deaf mutes, what was Atatürk's riposte?

10. The Emperor Charles V's victory at the Battle of Mühlberg in 1547 was a temporary setback for which cause?

11. Which British cabinet minister resigned over Chamberlain's conciliatory approaches to Mussolini after Italy's annexation of Abyssinia?

12. Which undistinguished American Civil War general gave his name to a species of facial hair?

13. What did Brian Clough, then manager of Derby County, say when he was shown Gavrilo Princip's footprints in the pavement at Sarajevo?

14. What was Louis XVI's surprising diary entry for 14 July 1789?

**QUIZ 42**

1. Who, according to Sir Herbert Samuel, was 'the ruling class's ideal candidate for imposing a balanced budget at the expense of the working class' during the National Government of 1931–5?

2. What did Queen Victoria say to Alick York, a flamboyant member of her household, when she overheard him telling a risqué story?

3. Which historic meeting took place between two German economists at the Café de la Régence in Paris in August 1844?

4. Which famous directional exhortation was first uttered by John Babonne Lane Soule in the Terre Haute, Indiana, *Express* in 1851?

5. Who was commissioned to make death masks of the most famous victims of Madame la Guillotine during the French Revolution?

6. Which country complained bitterly about its *vittoria mutilata* after World War I?

7. Which 1852 US invention made building skyscrapers practicable?

8. How did cynics refer to the notoriously blinkered Parliamentary Select Committee inquiry into the Jameson Raid of 1895–6?

9. Which US Civil War general further popularized a slang word for a woman engaged in the oldest profession?

10. Who was made Supreme Dictator and first President of Chile in 1817 after his defeat of the Spanish at Chacubuco?

11. Where was Sir Louis Cavagnari killed on 3 September 1879?

12. What did the American engineer Hiram Maxim pioneer in 1883?

13. What did Anton Drexler found in 1919?

14. Who opposed the pro-papal Guelphs in Italy during the thirteenth and fourteenth centuries?

# QUIZ 43

1.  Which prime minister was perceived as having betrayed his ideals and class by his friendship with the socialite Lady 'Circe' Londonderry?

2.  What is the link between the Roman emperors Septimus Severus, Gordianus I, Hostilanus and Valerianus?

3.  How did the Marquis de Lafayette ensure Napoleon's second and final abdication after his defeat at Waterloo?

4.  Who wrote *The Situation of the Working Class in England* in 1844?

5.  What was Francis Scott Key moved to write when he witnessed the awesome sight of shrapnel shells bursting over Baltimore during the 1812 War with Britain?

6.  Which Italian founding father, described as 'a man of genius and virtue' (Carlyle) and 'the man I venerate most' (Nietzsche), was exiled by the newly created monarchy and died in hiding in Pisa?

7.  How did the burning of lewd pictures, gaming tables, jewellery and books by Savonarola in Florence in 1497 become known?

8.  What did Pedro Cabral discover *en route* to India on 22 April 1500?

9.  When the notoriously corrupt MP Horatio Bottomley heard that F. E. Smith had been appointed Lord Chancellor, he congratulated him, saying, 'I shouldn't have been surprised to hear you'd also been made Archbishop of Canterbury.' What was F. E.'s waspish reply?

10. Who ruined diarist John Evelyn's famous holly hedge at Sayes Court in 1698?

11  What did Mr Chubb buy as a present for his wife in 1915?

12. Who were the Decembrists in Russian history?

13. What was agreed by the so-called appeasers at Munich on 29 September 1938?

14. Which Irish political party was founded by Arthur Griffith in 1902?

1. Why did Edvard Beneš resign the presidency of Czechoslovakia in September 1938?

2. What happened to Britain in c. 6500 BC?

3. 'An armour against enjoyment and a spider's web against danger.' What was the celebrated letter-writer Mme de Sévigné describing in a letter to her daughter in 1671?

4. What did the Dominican monk Johann Tetzel peddle in Jüterbog and Wittenberg in 1517?

5. Who cut the Gordian knot in 333 BC?

6. What did Keir Hardy say when he opposed a parliamentary motion to congratulate Queen Victoria on the birth of her great-grandson, the future Edward VIII, in June 1894?

7. Which Tsar was rumoured to have faked his own death and escaped to Siberia to live as a hermit under the name of Ivan Kuzmich?

8. Who marched on Rome on 28 October 1922?

9. Which war, according to the historian and Liberal MP J. A. Hobson, was started 'to place a small international oligarchy of mine-owners and speculators in power'?

10. When Winston Churchill was a young subaltern, an overpowering lady told him that she cared for neither his politics nor his moustache. What did he reply?

11. What was the bizarre and notorious ninth-century Cadaveric Synod or Synod Horrenda?

12. Which fifteenth-century nobleman was known as 'the Kingmaker'?

13. Who was the female link between the young Tudor gallants Thomas Culpeper and Francis Dereham?

14. What is the longest march in military history?

# QUIZ 45

1. Which two kings performed the dynastic see-saw during the first part of the Wars of the Roses?

2. How did Winston Churchill respond to a strident American matron who demanded of him at a diplomatic reception, 'What are you going to do about those wretched Indians?'

3. How is the epoch from c. AD 500 to 1000 generally termed?

4. Who founded the Seleukid Empire?

5. What, according to Lloyd George, was 'Mr Balfour's Poodle'?

6. What is the link between James Stephen, Montague John Druitt, James Maybrick, Sir William Gull, Aaron Kosminski and Michael Ostrog?

7. When Otto Abetz, Hitler's ambassador in occupied Paris, saw a print of *Guernica* hanging in Picasso's studio, he asked the painter if he had done it. What was Picasso's reply?

8. Who surprised whom at the Mukden Incident on 18 September 1931?

9. Who gave his name to an 'ism' for extreme Germanophobia in the years leading up to World War II?

10. Which American president was married to a virago of a wife who hit him with a broomstick, threw coffee in his face and generally made his life miserable with her violent rages and temper tantrums?

11. Who was Rudyard Kipling attacking in his poem entitled 'Gehazi'?

12. Which of Charles II's advisers made the word 'cabal' part of the English language?

13. Which general betrayed his country by conspiring with Major John André to deliver their key position at Westpoint to the British during the American War of Independence?

14. Which famous violinist refused to play the Fascist anthem, *Giovinezza*, at a party gathering in Bologna in June 1931?

# Answers

# ANSWERS TO QUIZ 1

1. Francisco Franco. He finally made his commitment to the rebellion after the assassination of the rightist politician José Calvo Sotelo.

2. The Decree of Papal Infallibility was pronounced by the Vatican Council on 18 July 1870. Pope Pius IX was therefore the first pope to enjoy infallibility in defining doctrines on faith and morals that became 'unalterable in themselves and not by virtue of the assent of the Church'.

3. He pronounced the list incomplete and calmly added his own name at the bottom in capital letters. He then asked his mother what punishment she thought suitable for these crimes. 'They must be burned,' she said vehemently. So Ferdinando flung the list into a nearby fire, saying, 'There they are, madam, punished even as you condemned them.'

4. Lenin, his wife, his mistress Inessa Armand, and twenty-nine other exiles left Zurich in the famous 'Sealed Train' on 9 April 1917 to cross Germany and then travel north along the Swedish Baltic coast to St Petersburg. The German foreign secretary, Arthur Zimmerman, had decided, 'It is in our interests that the influence of the radical wing of the Russian Revolutionaries should prevail.' But he was anxious that the Bolsheviks should be sealed in so they could not contaminate the German people with their ideology.

5. Not primarily to abolish slavery, but to preserve the Union after the secession of South Carolina and six other Southern states. 'My paramount object in this struggle is to save the Union, and not either to save or to destroy slavery. If I could save the union without freeing any slave, I would do it, if I could save it by freeing all the slaves I would do it' (letter to Horace Greeley dated 22 August 1862). But earlier he had expressed his abolitionist sentiments with the declaration, 'Let us draw a cordon around the slave states and the hateful institution, like a reptile poisoning itself, will perish by its own infamy.'

6. Carolus Linnaeus.

7. The poet Christopher Marlowe.

8. 'What's that?' he said in mock alarm. The unfortunate Biggar was a hunch-backed pork butcher, with a grating voice, bony hands, huge feet and a 'face like a gargoyle'.

9. Thomas Cook. Teetotal Cook then signed up 165,000 people for a tour of the Great Exhibition in 1851.

10. The *Manchester Guardian*. Founded in 1821, it set out to 'zealously enforce the principles of civil and religious liberty'.

11. General Kitchener and General Marchand defused a crisis in north-east Sudan when a French expedition occupied Fashoda. Marchand was politely persuaded, over coffee and liqueurs on Kitchener's gunboat, to withdraw in the face of Kitchener's immensely superior forces.

12. Liberal Party dissenters, led by the albino lawyer Robert Lowe and Lord Elcho, opposed to Gladstone's (electoral) Reform Bill of 1866. The word was coined by the radical MP John Bright from King David's followers in the 'Cave of Adullam', which 'housed everyone that was in distress and everyone that was discontented' (First Book of Samuel).

13. Phineas T. Barnum.

14. Charles Stewart Parnell. When they finally married in June 1891, after a messy divorce, Irish Roman Catholics were further outraged. The Bishop of Raphoe declared that the marriage 'only caps a climax of brazen horrors'. Parnell died of a coronary thrombosis in October of that same year.

# ANSWERS TO QUIZ 2

1. After the British torched it during the War of 1812 it lay derelict until 1817, when it was rebuilt and refurbished. Washingtonians admired its new coat of white paint, which had been applied to hide the scorch marks, and started to refer to it as the White House.

2. With an exaggeratedly courteous bow, Wilkes replied, 'Since I had the pleasure of Your Royal Highness's acquaintance.'

3. A plot by Whig extremists to assassinate Charles II and his brother, James, Duke of York. The two leaders, Lord William Russell and Algernon Sidney, were executed.

4. Simon de Montfort, with the help of the barons, captured Henry III and for a year ruled England in his name until he himself was killed at the Battle of Evesham.

5. 1536, through the Act of Union.

6. He was Jean-Baptiste Bernadotte, Prince of Pontecorvo, one of Napoleon's most brilliant marshals. As governor of the conquered Hanseatic cities he became friendly with some influential Swedish prisoners-of-war at Lübeck. In September 1810 the Swedish parliament unanimously elected Bernadotte Crown Prince of Sweden to succeed the childless Charles XIII. The Swedes wanted an alliance with Napoleon and may have been influenced by rumours of Bernadotte's enormous wealth. But as Crown Prince Jean-Baptiste is thought to have advised Tsar Alexander not to negotiate with Napoleon after the Battle of Borodino and to evacuate Moscow – the subsequent disastrous retreat from Moscow was the beginning of the end for the French emperor. Bernadotte tried to keep faith with his native country by refusing to fight on French soil and he declined an invitation to advance with the victorious Allies into France after Waterloo. Tsar Alexander also wanted Bernadotte to take the throne of France rather than restore the Bourbons.

7. The Dragon Empress, or Cixi. She was a concubine of the Emperor Hsien Feng and bore his only living son. On his death she became Dowager Empress and ruled China for nearly half a century.

8. 'Ladies never move.'

9. Henry I. He captured Robert, Duke of Normandy, at the Battle of Tinchebrai in 1106. There is strong evidence that Henry connived in the attempted murder of his other brother, William II.

10. They were all Frankish kings except Charles the Bad, who was a King of Navarre, and Charles the Bold, who was a particularly aggressive Duke of Burgundy.

11. Hong Kong, which was ceded 'in perpetuity to Her Britannic Majesty, her heirs and successors'. In 1982, during negotiations over sovereignty, the Chinese government insisted that the treaty (and the later treaties which had leased Kowloon and the New Territories) had been imposed upon the local officials of the Qing dynasty at the muzzle of a gun (in the aftermath of the Opium Wars), and were therefore illegal and invalid.

12. Winston Churchill. It was one of the last cavalry charges – if not the last – of the British Army.

13. His skilful steering of the second Reform Bill through Parliament. After Gladstone's failure to get his 1866 Reform Bill through the House of Commons and his subsequent resignation, Disraeli stole his thunder by dint of some brilliant and ruthless politicking. His bill turned out to be more radical than the Gladstone/Lord John Russell bill, enfranchising 1,000,000 men – in effect, household suffrage. That success made him the most likely man to succeed Lord Derby as prime minister. Robert Blake, in his biography of Disraeli, observes, 'For what he did in 1867 he deserves to go down to history as a politician of genius, a superb improviser, a parliamentarian of unrivalled skill, but not as a far-sighted statesman, a Tory democrat or the educator of his party.'

14. Charles Lynch, a planter and JP from Virginia. He was a patriot who headed an irregular court formed during the American War of Independence (or American Revolution) to punish loyalists.

# ANSWERS TO QUIZ 3

1. Amy Robsart. Although her husband, Elizabeth I's favourite, the Earl of Leicester, was cleared of her murder, the queen imprisoned him in the Tower for a short time.

2. The Althing in Iceland, founded in AD 930.

3. Kaiser Wilhelm II. But this is at variance with his earlier declaration, 'Jews and mosquitoes are a nuisance that humanity must get rid of in some way or other – I believe the best would be gas.'

4. Herbert Asquith. At the height of World War I the besotted prime minister would on occasions write to Venetia three times a day. When she became close to another minister, Edwin Montagu, both he and Asquith wrote to her during one wartime Cabinet meeting.

5. Catherine the Great.

6. 'Palmerston is now seventy-nine. If he could provide evidence of his potency in his electoral address, he'd sweep the country.' The lady in question was a Mrs Cane. London clubland joked, 'She was certainly Cane, but was he Abel?'

7. Leonardo da Vinci's *Mona Lisa*.

8. Police Commissioner Theodore Roosevelt prohibited the selling of liquor to hotels only on Sundays. A hotel was defined as a structure with ten bedrooms. When a local furniture store offered to furnish ten bedrooms for only $81.20 it did brisk business, and by the end of 1896 there were 2,000 new 'hotels' in the city. One converted its stable stalls into bedrooms and put up a sign over the bar stating, 'Sleeping in this hotel Positively Prohibited'.

9. Captain Charles Cunningham Boycott.

10. The sinister Cesare Borgia, illegitimate son of Pope Alexander VI. Machiavelli was aware of his many failings, but admired his mastery of the political and military manoeuvre, his opportunism and his daring.

11. Nero. He was certainly not fiddling, as the fiddle was not invented until the tenth century. Most historians have absolved him of the crime of arson in order to indulge his aesthetic pretensions to build a new Rome. In fact, according to some accounts, he tried to put the fire out.

12. Wellington and Napoleon.

13. Byron. His doctors removed more than four pounds of blood in an attempt to relieve a fever. They purged him with a ghastly concoction of senna, Epsom salts and castor oil, finally finishing him off by the application of leeches to his temple. By then Byron was unconscious and powerless to resist their ministrations. He had earlier referred to them as 'a damned bunch of butchers'.

14. During the research and development phase in 1914–15, for the purpose of secrecy it was referred to as a (water) tank in letters and reports. During the war the vehicles were transported to the front in crates labelled 'water tank'.

# ANSWERS TO QUIZ 4

1. The Duke of Wellington. The Countess of Mornington was his mother.

2. The Pilgrimage of Grace, the armed uprising in six northern English counties protesting against the Henrician (VIII) reforms generally and in the main against the Dissolution of the Monasteries in 1536. Aske wanted to remove Thomas Cromwell and give the north a say in the affairs of the nation and reverse certain policies. Aske, along with Lord Thomas Darcy, was executed. Aske had done everything possible to avoid bloodshed: only one man was killed during the pilgrimage.

3. To encourage settlers. It worked. Some 3,000 hardy people did eventually settle there and the settlement lasted around 500 years. The whole of the interior of Greenland is covered by an ice-cap.

4. The Sicilian Vespers. It was sparked off by the importuning of a young Sicilian woman by a drunken French sergeant called Drouet outside the church of the Santo Spirito on Easter Monday. Her furious husband stabbed him to death and when his fellow soldiers attempted to avenge the killing, as the church bells pealed to announce Vespers, a horrific massacre of the French ensued until 2,000 French men, women, children and priests had been slaughtered.

5. He married Shoshi, the beautiful seventeen-year-old mistress of his grandfather, the ex-emperor Sirakawa. Shoshi was conveniently pregnant by his grandpapa.

6. The government of the Ottoman Empire. It was named after the great gate giving access to the buildings of the state departments in what was then Constantinople.

7. Cymbeline, King of the Catuvellauni.

8. Viscount Trenchard, Commander of the Royal Flying Corps from 1915 to 1918. He became the first Marshal of the Royal Air Force in 1927.

9. Lord Kitchener. The general was on his way to Arkhangelsk (Archangel) for secret negotiations with Russian leaders. When the

newspaper proprietor Lord Northcliffe heard the news, he observed rather unfeelingly, 'Providence is on the side of the British Empire after all.'

10. 'Bossom? Bossom? What an extraordinary name – neither one thing nor the other!'

11. The Habsburg Archduke Maxmilian, who with the aid of Napoleon III was installed as puppet emperor of Mexico in 1862. He was later abandoned to his fate by Napoleon, captured by the army of former president Benito Juárez and executed by firing-squad.

12. Julius Caesar defeated Pompey and established his supremacy over the Roman world.

13. A league of Serbian boyars under the leadership of Prince Lazar Hrebeljanović, who had seized control of northern Serbia to resist Sultan Murad I's advance into the Balkans. The boyars were successful at first, but on 28 June they were defeated at Kosovo, 'the Field of Blackbirds'. The Serbian nation was annihilated; it lay dormant for just over 400 years. The battle inspired one of the great medieval epics, *The Kosovo Cycle*, and Lazar became one of the great legendary Serbian heroes, not least because he was later captured and executed by the Ottomans.

14. Pyotr Arkadyevich Stolypin, Tsar Nicholas II's prime minister. The assassin was a revolutionary named Mordka Bogrov.

## ANSWERS TO QUIZ 5

1. Gladstone. He won the election. She also described him as a 'half-mad firebrand'.

2. Abdul Hamid II, 'the Damned'. He was also known as 'the Old Spider' and, because of his role in the Armenian Massacres of 1894–6, 'the Great Assassin'.

3. Field-Marshal Paul von Hindenburg. In 1933 he appointed Adolf Hitler Chancellor.

4. Mary Tudor, often referred to as 'Bloody Mary'.

5. He was finding warmth and comfort in the arms of a certain Mrs Loring in nearby Philadelphia during the freezing winter of 1777–8. He disobeyed an order to attack at the beginning of March and was replaced by the equally timorous Sir Henry Clinton at the beginning of May. Meanwhile, Washington's army, while wintering at Valley Forge in conditions of extreme discomfort, had been drilled into an efficient fighting force.

6. After President Theodore 'Teddy' Roosevelt. During a hunting trip up the Mississippi in 1902 he refused to shoot a bearcub. An enterprising Brooklyn shopkeeper called Morris Mitchom, inspired by Clifford Berryman's subsequent *Washington Evening Star* cartoon, renamed his toy bears Teddy Bears.

7. The peace imposed by Britain and her empire upon hostile nations lasted from 1795 until the time of the Boer Wars. The notion echoed the Pax Romana and was popularized by Lord Palmerston in the 1840s and 1850s.

8. The first theatre showing of a moving picture. Although they were not the sole inventors of cinematography, they pioneered the photographic machine and projector which produced sixteen frames per second.

9. Marco Polo.

10. The *Mona Lisa*. Attendance figures at the Louvre shot up during its two-year absence. Evidently the public were far more fascinated by

the empty space than by the actual picture. Perugia kept the picture hidden in a trunk for those two years before it was discovered.

11. In 776 BC, at the confluence of the rivers Alpheus and Cladeus at Olympia.

12. A small villa in Versailles which housed working-class girls to service the king's sexual needs. His relationship with Madame de Pompadour became platonic after 1751 and she seemed entirely happy and less fatigued with this new arrangement. 'Cerf' means 'deer'.

13. 'Died, has he? Now I wonder what he meant by that?'

14. Prince Charles.

## ANSWERS TO QUIZ 6

1. The Battle of Jutland on 31 May 1916. The only major sea battle of World War I, it was indecisive, bloody (nearly 8,000 lives were lost), and dogged by poor communications. But it marked the end of German control of the North Sea.

2. François Toussaint L'Ouverture. Born a slave, he was the leader of the Haitian independence movement against the French and founded the first black republic. Eventually an ally of Napoleon himself, he was betrayed by him, captured and died in a dank French prison in 1803.

3. It probably derived from Oliver Cromwell's imprisonment of Royalist sympathizers in Coventry during the Civil War.

4. El Cid.

5. His insistence that the four bronze horses looted by Napoleon from St Mark's Square in Venice should be returned there, and that the many other works of art looted from various other European cities should be returned to their place of origin. The early Roman statues had in turn been looted by the Venetians from Constantinople in 1205.

6. Europe: she was called Europa.

7. Hippocrates (460–377 BC).

8. They were the first leaders to embrace the tenets of Martin Luther's Reformation. Along with the cities of Nuremberg, Strasburg, Ulm, Augsburg and others.

9. Mata Hari – Malay, meaning 'eye of the morning'. The proud citizens of her home town, Leeuwarden, have recently opened a museum to her memory displaying nude photographs, love letters and stage costumes.

10. 'Steadily towards women and drink, Mr President.' F. E.'s terse reply reflected his dislike of Wilson.

11. The Frankish Emperor Clovis. He therefore gave France her name, her religion and her capital city.

12. Charles II.

13. The Republic (509–27 BC) and the Empire (27 BC–AD 476).

14. John Wilkes.

# ANSWERS TO QUIZ 7

1.  The six Lutheran princes named in Quiz 6 and the fourteen cities that issued a Protestation against the second Imperial Diet of Speyer (1529), which reneged on the earlier Diet's promise to allow the princes freedom of religious self-determination within their own territories. The term was used initially by their Catholic opponents only.

2.  Madame du Barry.

3.  Richard II, after he had been deposed by Bolingbroke, who later became King Henry IV.

4.  Henry VIII.

5.  They were both traduced by their daughters. James's daughters were of course Queen Mary and Queen Anne.

6.  The mutiny on the cruiser *Potemkin*, led by Afanasy Matushenko, at Odessa in July 1905. A sailor had complained of maggot-ridden meat in their bortsch; the incident escalated into a revolt.

7.  'By God, Mr Chairman, at this moment I stand astonished at my own moderation.' He committed suicide in 1774.

8.  On the eve of the battle Constantine claimed to have seen a vision of a cross of light which bore the inscription 'Conquer with this'. He resolved to worship the God who had been revealed to him, and gave orders that the symbol of the imperial eagle should be replaced by the sign of the cross. He subsequently attributed his victory over Maxentius to his conversion to Christianity.

9.  The Persian King Darius III. Alexander then proceeded to conquer the Persian territories of Damascus, Tyre, Jerusalem and Egypt.

10. The Battle of Rossbach, Frederick the Great's victory over a Franco-Austrian force during the Seven Years War, which changed the destiny of Germany.

11. Charles V's 15,000-strong army of unpaid German mercenaries during the Italian Wars. In eight days thousands of churches, palaces and houses were pillaged, effectively ending the city's pre-eminence as a Renaissance centre. It was Charles's retaliation against the formation of the Holy League a year before.

12. The liberal Emperor Frederick of Germany, son-in-law of Queen Victoria, and father of Kaiser Wilhelm.

13. Boudicca.

14. They were the only nine of the fifty-nine men who signed Charles I's death warrant to be hanged, drawn and quartered after the Restoration of Charles II.

# ANSWERS TO QUIZ 8

1.  They were all conspirators in the July Plot of 1944 to assassinate Adolf Hitler. Hitler demanded they be 'hung like cattle', and eight of them were hung from meat-hooks in Berlin's Plotzensee Prison. The execution chamber is now a permanent memorial to them.

2.  King William III and Queen Mary.

3.  When Henri II of France unwisely confided in him his own and his fellow Catholic monarch Philip II of Spain's scheme to exterminate heresy by massacring all French and Dutch Protestants. Henri believed William a party to the plot. He wasn't. And William, who had been brought up in a Lutheran household until he was eleven, revealed none of the horror and revulsion he felt. He bided his time until April 1567, when he resigned from the court of Philip's sister, the Regent Margaret, at Brussels and retired to his German estate at Dillenburg. Meanwhile the Spanish army of the brutal Duke of Alba (or Alva) was marching menacingly towards the Netherlands. In July 1572 William crossed the Rhine at Duisburg into the province of Gelderland and headed towards Brussels, vowing, 'I have come to make my grave in this land.'

4.  King Ludwig II of Bavaria.

5.  King James II when Duke of York. His succession of plain mistresses were a great source of amusement to the court of Charles II. His cousin Louis, the Grand Dauphin (Louis XIV's eldest son), had the same quirk. His fiancée, Victoire of Bavaria, was found to be so ugly that Louis was willing to extricate his son from the engagement. But unaccountably the Dauphin was strongly attracted to her bulbous nose, red hands and rotten teeth, and fell besottedly in love. After her death the Dauphin fell in love with a lady-in-waiting called Marie-Thérèse Joly de Choin, who was fat and snub-nosed. She also had very large, pendulous breasts, on which he used to beat a tattoo with his fingers. They later married in secret.

6.  The last Roman legion left.

7.  King Charles XII of Sweden at the beginning of the Great Northern War.

8. Maastricht. It was an action that led directly to the War of the Spanish Succession.

9. He called upon the princes of Western Europe to put aside all other concerns and set out for the Holy Land to win back Jerusalem for Christianity (thus beginning the First Crusade).

10. Charlemagne.

11. Anne Boleyn on the eve of her execution. She had probably been spared a more painful and protracted death.

12. The Parthenon. A mortar Morosini had placed on the Mouseion Hill just opposite the Acropolis was fired by a German lieutenant at the Parthenon. Unfortunately the building was being used as an ammunition dump by the Turks and the mortar scored a direct hit.

13. It is usually dated at 586 BC when King Nebuchadnezzar deported prominent Jews *en masse* to Babylon (the Babylonian Captivity) after his conquest of Jerusalem and the destruction of the first Temple. Many other Israelites fled north to Samaria, Edom and Moab, or south to Egypt. There was an earlier dispersal in 733 BC, when the Assyrians carried off thousands of the elite of northern Israel, who were then assimilated into the local population of the Assyrian Empire.

14. The Carthaginian army of Hannibal vanquished the Roman army. At Lake Trasimene 15,000 Romans and their allies died in what was the greatest reversal of Roman arms that had ever occurred. At Cannae 45,000 Romans were killed. Many years later Livy wrote, 'No other nation could have suffered such a tremendous disaster and not been destroyed.' And Leonard Cottrell, in his *Enemy of Rome*, points out that 'This ghastly toll of lives, the result of a few hours' fighting, is greater than the total number of men killed in the Royal Air Force throughout the First and Second World Wars.'

## ANSWERS TO QUIZ 9

1.  It was rumoured by gossips in Vienna that he was too exhausted to attend to diplomatic business after spending the night with his current mistress, Wilhelmine de Sagan (sister of Talleyrand's long-time mistress, the Duchess of Dino).

2.  Julius Caesar.

3.  His great-grandson. Louis XIV's son, the Grand Dauphin, the only one of his children to survive infancy, had died of smallpox. His grandson, the Duc de Bourgogne, his grandson's wife, Marie-Adelaide, and their eldest son also died of smallpox. Three dauphins died in eleven months. The two-year-old Louis (later Louis XV) was infected but his sensible governess saved his life by removing him from the deadly ministrations of the court doctors.

4.  Bismarck during his speech to the Prussian House of Delegates (the Landtag) in Berlin on becoming Chancellor. 'Iron and blood' was later reversed to the more euphonius 'blood and iron'. He practised what he preached: within eight years he had humbled Denmark, Austria and France. He may not have known that he was quoting the Roman rhetorician Quintilian, who used the phrase 'sanguinem et ferrum'.

5.  The document proving the legitimacy of the Duke of Monmouth, probably the marriage certificate, dated 1648 in Liège, of the young Charles II and his mistress, Lucy Walter. (Monmouth married Anne, Duchess of Buccleuch and the pair were created Duke and Duchess of Buccleuch.) In the face of court intrigues to put Monmouth on the throne, Charles decided to refute the rumours officially in the *London Gazette* in 1680. The fifth duke good-naturedly threw the document into Queen Victoria's fire saying, 'That might cause of lot of trouble.'

6.  King Philip II of Macedon, father of Alexander the Great.

7.  'I cannot tell, but that is what I am trying to find out.'

8.  The Seven Years War.

9. During the so-called 'Glorious Revolution' of December 1688 to February 1689, when James II fled from England, thereby in effect abdicating, and William III and Mary were established as joint monarchs.

10. The Crimean War.

11. 'The Rough Wooing', because one of Henry's prime aims was to arrange the marriage of his son, Edward, to the infant Mary, Queen of Scots. The invasion of 1544 by Edward Seymour and John Dudley left Edinburgh in flames.

12. Nancy, Lady Astor. The Countess Markiewicz had been elected a Sinn Fein MP in 1918, but refused to take her seat.

13. It was the period in which Charles I ruled without Parliament – acknowledged by many historians as a time of relative peace and prosperity.

14. Ernest, Duke of Cumberland. According to Cumberland, Sellis had attempted to murder him and had then cut his own throat. The jury returned a verdict of suicide, but there were rumours of a confession by the duke hidden away in the royal archives. The incident is still shrouded in mystery, but the most likely motive for the attempted murder is the Corsican Roman Catholic Sellis's bitter hatred of his virulently anti-Catholic master. The duke was said to have fathered a child on his own sister, Sophia. This was a lie: it was actually sired by a General Garth and the pregnancy was passed off as dropsy – at least for a while.

## ANSWERS TO QUIZ 10

1.  Julius Caesar.

2.  In 1688 when William of Orange and his army marched in triumph to London after the flight of James II. William ordered all British troops to withdraw twenty miles outside the capital.

3.  1666 – though wonders seemed pretty thin on the ground, what with the Great Plague the year before, the Great Fire of London and some rather inconclusive naval encounters with the Dutch.

4.  In November 1871 the radical MP Sir Charles 'Three-in-a-Bed' Dilke attacked Queen Victoria during a speech in Newcastle, accusing her of dereliction of duty after Albert's death, and advocated that she be deposed and a republic set up. The clamour subsided the following month with popular relief over the Prince of Wales's recovery from typhoid. Income tax was also mentioned.

5.  The Bolshevik Revolution, from 17 November 1917.

6.  William Gladstone. He failed to get them through parliament because of Conservative opposition.

7.  That the Kaiser would give the Austrians his unconditional support in any move they might make against Serbia after the assassination of Archduke Franz Ferdinand at Sarajevo.

8.  The Byzantine Empire.

9.  Napoleon III. He escaped after five years and in 1848 became President of France. He later made both sons counts of the Second Empire. (Alexandrine was nicknamed 'La Sabotière' because she was a talented clog dancer.)

10. During the first century AD, probably through Roman soldiers, but the religion was later overwhelmed by the invasions of pagan Anglo-Saxons. The faith survived in Wales and parts of the West Country.

11. Pope Gregory I (or Gregory the Great), who gave the Church its public services and its sacred chants.

12. The Norwegian Roald Amundsen.

13. The Vandals, led by King Gaiseric (or Genseric). They had promised Pope Leo I that they would not destroy the city or kill its citizens. For two weeks they systematically stripped Rome of its wealth, its statues and ornaments, which they carried off back to Carthage. But they kept their promise and spared the Romans' lives and their actual buildings.

14. Girolamo Savonarola.

## ANSWERS TO QUIZ 11

1.  John Montagu, Earl of Sandwich, who rejoiced in the nickname of
    'Jeremy Twitcher' (after the character in John Gay's *The Beggar's
    Opera* who was a false friend – Sandwich had supposedly betrayed
    John Wilkes through his role in Wilkes's prosecution). In fact Martha
    Ray was his mistress for seventeen years and bore him five children.
    She was also an accomplished singer. She was shot by a madman
    called James Hackman outside Covent Garden theatre. Sandwich's
    wife was a certified lunatic.

2.  When young Peter (the Great) ruled with his sickly half-brother Ivan
    for seven years from 1682. At the age of sixteen Peter grabbed the
    reins of power from his sister, the Regent Sophia, and banished her to
    a nunnery.

3.  The empire created by the Saxon Otto I (the Great) from the warring
    German duchies in 936. His victory over the Magyars (Hungarians) at
    the River Lech in 955 and his subjugation of the Slavs in 960 con-
    solidated his position. He was crowned Holy Roman Emperor (he is
    often considered the first Holy Roman Emperor) by Pope John XII in
    962. Otto's descendants ruled until 1024, supporting the Church to
    balance the nobles' ambitions, which led to the so-called Ottonian
    Renaissance.

4.  When Pope Gregory VII excommunicated Holy Roman Emperor
    Henry IV for flouting his authority over the investiture of the
    Archbishop of Milan. Henry called a synod and deposed Gregory; but
    lacking support from his own princes he had to back down. Henry's
    capitulation in 1076 was enacted when in pentinent's garb he walked
    barefoot in the snow (having waited three days) to eat humble pie
    before Gregory at Canossa Castle in northern Italy. 'Canossa saw
    Europe's mightiest prince, titular lord of the world, a suppliant before
    the successor of the Apostle,' according to the *Encyclopaedia
    Britannica*. 'Relations between Church and state were changed
    forever.'

5.  Alfred the Great, King of Wessex, forced the Danish invaders to sign
    a treaty which divided Britain into a Saxon Wessex and a Danish
    north-east (including Northumbria, East England and the East
    Midlands). The peace did not hold.

6. After a tribe called the Rus (otherwise known as the Varangarians), descendants of Swedish Vikings, who opened up north-east trade routes to the Baltic and the Black Sea, establishing their capital at Novogorod. 'Varang' is an old Norse word meaning 'plighted faith'.

7. The Battle of Poltava (Ukraine) between Sweden and Russia, during the Great Northern War – it marked the emergence of Peter the Great's Russia as a major European power; and the Battle of Malplaquet between the British–Dutch alliance and France during the War of the Spanish Succession.

8. Napoleon.

9. Kaiser Wilhelm II.

10. The Ottoman – approximately 200 years longer (1300 to 1924).

11. 'Follow me.'

12. St Alban, born in either 254 or 209.

13. Charles V, the most powerful ruler of his era. The son of Joanna of Castile (also known as Joanna the Mad, or Juana la Loca) and Philip of Burgundy, he inherited from his paternal grandfather, the Emperor Maximilian, the vast Habsburg domains of the Netherlands, Burgundy and the kingdoms of Naples, Sicily and Sardinia. He had already inherited Spain and its territories in the New World from his maternal grandfather, King Ferdinand.

14. Samuel Johnson.

# ANSWERS TO QUIZ 12

1. William Pitt the Elder, later Lord Chatham.

2. It marked the final schism between the Roman Church and the Eastern Orthodox Church. The hostility was aggravated when Humbert described a popular monk called Nicetas Stethatus as a 'pestiferous pimp'. The two Churches were briefly united in July 1274 at the Council of Lyon, when envoys of the Byzantine emperor, Michael Palaeologus, and Pope Gregory X acknowledged papal primacy. But anti-unionist protestors in the empire were angry when Gregory's successor, Pope Nicholas III, attempted to force all the Byzantine clergy to swear an oath of recognition of the primacy of the Roman Church. Michael had to invent a number of fictional bishops and forge their oaths.

3. She used it as kindling to light a fire.

4. John Churchill, Duke of Marlborough. By various methods Churchill had duped the timid French Marshal Villeroi into thinking he was going to march due south along the Moselle to invade France. The Duc de Saint-Simon said acidly of Villeroi that he was 'a man formed expressly to preside at a ball and, if he had a voice, to sing at the Opera...very well suited to lead the fashions and for nothing else'.

5. According to Tudor tradition, he refused to obey the order of Richard III to murder the Princes in the Tower (Edward IV's sons, Edward and Richard). Richard's defenders vehemently deny that Richard was responsible for the princes' deaths, and point out that there is no proof of exactly when or by whose hand they died.

6. Oxford.

7. Menes. He united Upper and Lower Egypt, the Nile Valley and Delta around 3,000 BC, establishing Memphis as his capital at the apex of the Nile.

8. Hannibal, while he was a guest of King Prusias. The Romans were closing in.

9. The Crimean War. One officer commented that Balaclava was run by 'a gang of raving lunatics'. Commander-in-Chief Lord Raglan, a

Waterloo veteran, had trouble remembering that this time the French were allies not enemies. During the Peninsular War the Duke of Wellington had been similarly encumbered with Sir William Erskine, who was drunken, 'blind as a beetle' and probably mad; he had been sent home 'indisposed' the year before. Generals Lumley and Lightburne and Colonel Landers were other causes for concern: 'I pray God and the Horse Guards to deliver me from General Lightburne and Colonel Landers,' moaned the distraught Wellington.

10. The Treaty of Paris in 1763, which brought to an end the Seven Years War. Britain gained Canada, America east of the Mississippi, Grenada, St Vincent, Dominica, Tobago, Florida and Minorca; also most of the French territories in India.

11. Because in translation it means 'I have sinned.'

12. James, Duke of York, later James II. Apropos of nothing, Nell Gwynn always used to refer to him behind his back as 'dismal Jimmy'.

13. Wilhelm Karl Roentgen, Professor of Physics at the University of Würzburg. 'X' for 'unknown'.

14. George V. The man who made the accusation, the arch-republican E. F. Mylius, was convicted of criminal libel and imprisoned for twelve months in 1911.

## ANSWERS TO QUIZ 13

1.  Abraham Lincoln's.

2.  Jesus Christ. We have to thank Dionysius Exiguus for the erroneous date of Christ's birth. The abbot, mathematician, astronomer and theologian was asked to prepare the Christian calendar or chronology by Pope John I in 525. He dated the birth using the Roman system, according to which it took place 754 years after the founding of Rome on 25 December 753 BC (i.e., on 25 December in the year AD 1). However, today it is generally accepted that Christ was born during Herod's reign – and Herod died in 4 BC. The date of c. 6 BC is now widely accepted, though some people believe that Christ may have been born as early as 12 BC.

3.  The Look, Duck and Vanish Brigade (or, alternatively, the Long-Dentured Veterans).

4.  The Greeks overwhelmed the Persians in both battles at this heroic moment in their history, bringing the long conflict with the Persians to an end and opening up the golden era of Greece.

5.  Richard Lloyd George, son of David Lloyd George.

6.  Damascus in Syria. Its origins can be traced back to the third millennium BC and it has been known by its present name since the fifteenth century BC.

7.  Karl Marx.

8.  He called it 'dephlogisticated air'. It was given its more familiar name, oxygen, by the great French chemist Antoine Lavoisier in 1789.

9.  Edward III.

10. Oliver Cromwell in 1653. 'Come, come, I will put an end to your prating. You are no Parliament. I say you are no Parliament. I will put an end to your sitting,' he shouted, and ordered his musketeers to clear the chamber. The subsequent short-lived Barebones Parliament was equally troublesome.

11. England.

12. Warren Hastings, former Governor-General of Bengal. In the end Burke persuaded the government to impeach Hastings on twenty charges of extortion and mismanagement, but he was eventually acquitted.

13. His plans for the submarine *Nautilus*. The French rejected it as an atrocious and dishonourable way to fight. Three years later it was built with government sanction, but it was never used.

14. 'The next time Mr Selwyn calls, show him up. If I am alive I shall be delighted to see him, and if I am dead he will be glad to see me.'

## ANSWERS TO QUIZ 14

1. Queen Marie-Amélie (de Bourbon-Sicile), wife of King Louis-Philippe.

2. He and two friends, 'being inflamed with strong liquor' after a session in the Cock Tavern, went out on to the balcony, pulled down their breeches and 'excremitized' into the street. Sedley then stripped naked and preached blasphemy to the crowd gathered below, who pelted him with rotten apples.

3. It was their defeat by the Seljuk Turks (under Sultan Alp Arslan), a defeat which 'resulted in the capture of the Emperor Romanus IV Diogenes, the ignominious flight of the once invincible Byzantine army and the gradual spread of the conquerors across Anatolia until some 30,000 square miles of the imperial heartland had been overrun by Turkoman tribesmen. At a stroke, Byzantium had lost the source of much of its food supply and most of its manpower. Its very survival was now in doubt.'* The empire had lost three-quarters of its valuable territory in that region; thus began its gradual decline and the rise of the Islamic empires.

4. Old Sarum had no houses in it, and Old Dunwich had been almost entirely submerged in the North Sea for centuries. They were just two of the 140 Rotten Boroughs, fifty of which had fewer than fifty voters. At that time Manchester and Birmingham were unrepresented in parliament.

5. They were spoken of the Charge of the Light Brigade, by an extremely hostile and irritated Captain Edward Nolan, who had just relayed Lord Raglan's attack order to Lord Lucan; Nolan absolutely despised Lucan. Lord Lucan then had to relay the order to his brother-in-law Lord Cardigan, whom he had absolutely despised for thirty years. 'Had the two men not detested each other so bitterly, had they been able to examine the order together and discuss its meaning, the Light Brigade might have been saved. Alas, thirty years of hatred could not be bridged.'†

6. Davy Crockett. One hundred and fifty Texans defended the fort of San Antonio against the 5,000-strong Mexican army of General Antonio López de Santa Anna.

7. Lloyd George in Newcastle in 1909, when he was Chancellor of the Exchequer.

8. The tomb of Tutankhamun, virtually intact after 3,274 years.

9. Edward I. In 1996 Prime Minister John Major announced that the Stone was to be returned to Scotland.

10. According to the latest carbon-dating 5,300 years old.

11. The ruthless Zulu king, Shaka.

12. Sir Francis Drake. The Portuguese explorer Ferdinand Magellan was hacked to death half-way round. Drake set sail from Plymouth in November 1577, and on 26 September 1580 the *Golden Hind* sailed back up Plymouth Sound on the flood tide. 'Is the Queen still alive?' Drake asked of a fisherman leaning over the ship's rail. She was, and she was happy to receive her share of the loot pirated from Spanish ships which probably amounted to the then vast sum of £160,000 (enough to meet her government's expenses for nearly a year).

13. 'That, Sire, is a question of dates.'

14. Messalina. 'A creature of shameless lust and remorseless cruelty',[‡] who donned a flaxen wig and 'drifted into unfamiliar vices' (as Tacitus rather euphemistically describes it) in a dingy Roman brothel. She forced Poppaea Sabina and the blameless Asiasticus to commit suicide (the former because she had filched Messalina's dancer lover Mnester, and the latter because she coveted his beautiful gardens).

* John Julius Norwich, *Byzantium: The Decline and Fall* (Viking)
† Cecil Woodham Smith, *The Reason Why* (Penguin)
‡ J. C. Stobart, *The Grandeur that was Rome* (Sidgwick & Jackson)

## ANSWERS TO QUIZ 15

1. The Battle of Valmy, the defeat of the Duke of Brunswick's Prussian force by the French Army of the Revolution under General Dumouriez.

2. The Inca king, Atahualpa. The ransom was paid in full. Many of the objects and jewellery were masterpieces of Inca craftsmanship – probably worth over £3 million today – which the Spanish melted down.

3. The army of Attila the Hun – his first and last defeat. Attila then retreated to Hungary, and the Hun menace to western Europe ended.

4. Louis XIV to his five-year-old great-grandson, soon to be proclaimed Louis XV.

5. Hannibal and the Roman general Publius Cornelius Scipio (Africanus). They 'were two of the most distinguished soldiers, not only of the ancient world, but of all time.'* Livy wrote later, 'Mutual admiration struck them dumb.' Shortly afterwards Hannibal was to suffer a terrible defeat at the Battle of Zama, the last engagement of the Second Punic War.

6. George V. He persuaded his government to withdraw their original offer of asylum, because 'he felt himself doubly menaced: by a whispering campaign that doubted his patriotism, and by an upsurge of republicanism. At just such a time of insecurity, his Government urged him to endorse their offer of sanctuary to the Imperial family, a gesture that would have identified him with Tsarist autocracy and imperilled his own repute as a constitutional monarch.'†

7. Josef Stalin.

8. Thomas Wentworth, Earl of Strafford, one of Charles I's ablest advisers. The only crime that John Pym and his coterie could come up with was that he gave his monarch unconstitutional advice. To restore harmony between the king and his subjects, Strafford himself wrote to Charles begging him to sign the Bill of Attainder. The king acquiesced but Strafford's death lay heavy on his conscience. When he himself was sent to the scaffold, Charles continued to protest his innocence of the charges made against him, but acknowledged, 'An

unjust sentence that I suffered to take effect, is punished now by an unjust sentence on me.' No one doubted that he was referring to Strafford.

9.  Sir Walter Ralegh's second attempt to found a colony on Roanoke Island, Virginia. (Elizabeth I would not allow Ralegh to go himself.) In July 1587, 115 colonists landed on the island. They simply disappeared, probably slaughtered by the braves of the despotic Indian chief Powhatan (father of Pocahontas) sometime in 1604 or 1605. Their deaths roughly coincided with the founding of the successful Jamestown settlement at nearby Chesapeake Bay.

10. Queen Christina of Sweden.

11. It ended with the deposition of the teenage Emperor Romulus Augustulus by the Goth King Odoacer at Ravenna. Imperial rule was maintained, at least nominally.

12. The elderly Sarah Churchill, wife of the first Duke of Marlborough.

13. Henri Christophe, who joined the revolt of slaves and mulatto landowners led by François Toussaint L'Ouverture in Haiti. He became a provisional leader and declared himself king in 1811. His regime was idealistic, but despotic. He shot himself in 1820.

14. Nero. He kissed her lovingly when she set sail on the Bay of Naples and waited impatiently for news of her death. (He had arranged for an escort vessel to ram her ship, in case Plan A failed.) But one of her attendants brought him the joyful news that after her ship had capsized his tough mama had been seen swimming strongly for the shore. She did not survive long, though, being bludgeoned and then stabbed to death on Nero's orders soon after her miraculous escape. Agrippina had got her just desserts, for she had arranged the deaths of (among others) her second husband, Passienus Crispus, and her sister-in-law Lollia Paulina, and had killed her third husband, the Emperor Claudius (who was also her uncle), with poisonous mushrooms.

* Ernle Bradford, *Hannibal* (Dorset)
† Kenneth Rose, *King George V* (Weidenfeld & Nicolson)

## ANSWERS TO QUIZ 16

1. They all killed, or were held directly responsible for the deaths of, their eldest sons. The dreadful Ottoman Sultan Ibrahim 'the Debauched' was declared insane by his mother and strangled.

2. Charlemagne's. In fact it had been crafted for Otto I, the first Holy Roman Emperor.

3. According to Goethe it was 'to avoid the daily task of dressing and undressing' (he did not name Boothby).

4. Lola Montez. She had a strong sexual magnetism, particularly for the 60-year-old King Ludwig I of Bavaria. The Bavarian Jesuits called her 'an Apocalyptic whore', and the staid citizens of Munich, outraged by her scandalous and arrogant behaviour, demanded she be ejected from the city. The poor sexually obsessed, but hitherto conscientious, Ludwig was forced to abdicate. She had earlier pursued Franz Liszt, who, desperate to evade her attentions, had to lock the determined virago in her hotel bedroom before he could make good his escape.

5. In England by English embroiderers, though it was probably of Norman design. It was commissioned by Bishop Odo, half-brother of William the Conqueror for the consecration of Bayeux Cathedral.

6. The English Commonwealth.

7. Henry V.

8. The Franco-Prussian War (1870–71). The Spanish crown had been offered to the Prussian Prince Leopold of Hohenzollern. Although Leopold refused it, the French government demanded a promise that there would be no further claims.

9. Mary, Queen of Scots.

10. Elizabeth I.

11. She was tormented by the delusion that she had swallowed a grand piano made of glass. King Charles VI of France, during his periodic fits of madness, was convinced that he was made of glass and forbade anyone to touch him.

## 16

12.  Newfoundland, which was claimed by John Cabot in 1497. However, it was used as a fishing ground for centuries, and was not properly settled until 1824.

13.  The English fight against the Spanish Armada. The English scattered the Armada off the Flemish coast on 29 July 1588.

14.  William the Silent. '. . . some men have a quality of greatness which gives their lives universal significance. Such men . . . exist to shame the cynic, and to renew the faith of humanity in itself. Of this number was William of Nassau, Prince of Orange, called the Silent.'* The kind-hearted William had lent the penniless Gérards twelve crowns. With this he bought, from one of William's own guards, the pistol that killed the great man.

* C. V. Wedgwood, *William the Silent* (Jonathan Cape)

# ANSWERS TO QUIZ 17

1. The Thirty Years War.

2. Charlemagne.

3. Emmeline Pankhurst.

4. Henri IV, France's most popular king, known by his people as the 'Vert-Galant' ('Evergreen Gallant').

5. Calamity Jane.

6. George V. There is no evidence that he carried out his threat.

7. The Inca King Atahualpa – in spite of his payment in full of the gold ransom (see Quiz 15 ). The poor man had to convert to Christianity to avoid being burnt to death.

8. Sir John Hawkins in 1565. But it was Sir Walter Ralegh who made it popular some twenty years later.

9. The Athenian politician Cleisthenes created the framework and administration of democracy. He broke the power of the tribes and the land-owning aristocrats by establishing ten political districts called *deme*s (or parishes) in terms of region rather than social status. It was probably Cleisthenes who began the practice of ostracism.

10. Three. Lord Liverpool resigned on 17 February 1827 after a stroke and he was succeeded by George Canning. Canning died of inflammation of the lung after only four months in office and was succeeded by Viscount Goderich, who served until 8 June 1828, when the Duke of Wellington took office for the first time.

11. Britain formally recognized the independence of the United States of America, two years after the surrender of General Cornwallis at Yorktown.

12. Arminius, chief of the Cherusci tribes. Although the defeat was later avenged, the old and feeble Emperor Augustus abandoned all hope of further conquest of German territory, muttering pathetically, 'Varus, give me back my legions.' Varus later committed suicide.

13. Marshal Josef Radetzky, later immortalized by Johann Strauss the Elder in his *Radetzky March*.

14. It comes from the ethnic 'Slav' or 'Sclavus', the swathe of untamed territory stretching eastwards from Germany and inhabited by the Slavs. It was the main source of slaves during the Dark Ages.

# ANSWERS TO QUIZ 18

1.  They were all second-born sons who succeeded to the throne after the deaths of their elder brothers.

2.  Alexander the Great's. Robin Lane Fox writes in his life of Alexander that 'it was not so much a mutiny as the expression of a deep despair': they had marched 11,250 miles in eight years. Had they agreed to advance Alexander could have conquered the ineffectual Dhana Nanda's kingdom of Magadha, annexed the whole of northern India, sailed down the Ganges and accomplished his dream of discovering the Eastern Ocean (the Bay of Bengal) only 600 miles away.

3.  Philip loathed his wife and persuaded Martin Luther to grant him a species of dispensation to marry his much younger mistress, Margaret van der Saale, bigamously on condition that he kept it secret. Unhappily for all concerned, the secret leaked out and the incident did considerable damage to Luther's reputation.

4.  George III.

5.  Emperor Charles I of Austria-Hungary.

6.  It implemented the Spanish-born Pope Alexander VI's ruling that any new-found lands of the Americas and the Orient west of a longitudinal line drawn 100 leagues west of the Azores should go to Spain. The lands to the east of it should belong to Portugal. 'The breathtaking arrogance of the two Catholic nations in simply dividing the world between them was never an issue.'* When the line was moved further west, Portugal was able to bag Brazil.

7.  Constantine the Great, who according to the historian Jacob Burckhardt had 'a cold and terrible lust for power'.

8.  General Pershing, leader of the American Expeditionary Force. Pershing denied having said 'anything so splendid' and the words have been attributed to his subordinate Colonel Charles Stanton.

9.  He produced a long, sharp barber's razor and cut off their beards. Thereafter beards were taxed, much as they had been in England during the reign of Elizabeth I. Peter was following a distinguished

precedent: Ivan Grozny ('the Terrible') had burnt off his boyars' beards with candles.

10. Henry VI of England.

11. Phidias.

12. The Aztecs of Mexico.

13. The followers of the Byzantine Emperor Leo III who condemned the veneration of icons as idolatrous or sacrilegious (from 726). The Emperor Michael III restored icon-worship in 843 and iconoclasm was declared a heresy.

14. Charlotte Sophia Kielmannsegge, otherwise known as 'the Elephant'.

* Simon Berthon and Andrew Robinson, *The Shape of the World* (IBM)

# ANSWERS TO QUIZ 19

1. Queen Mary, of William and Mary.

2. Samuel Morse.

3. Alexander the Great. He had been wounded in nine different places in the previous twelve years. His 'bravery which bordered on folly never failed him in the front line of battle, a position which few generals since have considered proper; he set out to show himself a hero, and from the Granicus to Multan he left a trail of heroics which has never been surpassed.'* The Greek historian Arrian wrote, 'There has never been another man in all the world, who by his own hand succeeded in so many brilliant enterprises.'

4. Sarah, Duchess of Marlborough.

5. Four. The 76-year-old Galba was butchered in the Forum after seven months. Then came the foppish Otho, a 'transient and embarrassed phantom', who was persuaded to commit suicide after only three months when he was usurped by the extremely beastly and extravagant Vitellius, who murdered his own son. 'The ghastly game of Roman roulette' as Stewart Perowne describes it in his *Caesars' Wives* came to an end, for the time being, with the arrival of Vespasian hotfoot from destroying Jerusalem. Vitellius was nearly savaged to death by a dog when he took refuge in its kennel and was later killed by Vespasian's soldiers and thrown into the Tiber. Vespasian was to become one of Rome's best rulers. Tacitus remarked that he was the only emperor whose character changed for the better.

6. Joan of Arc. Lorraine was not incorporated into France until 1776. The stories of her peasant origins are economical with the truth: her father was Domrémy's leading citizen.

7. During an attempt to capture the town of Santa Cruz on Tenerife from Spain in 1797.

8. Cato the Elder (234–149 BC). But Carthage was not finally destroyed until 146 BC. After a three-year siege it was razed to the ground in a fire that lasted seventeen days 'as an expiation of the *lemures* of the unburied Roman dead'.

9. Ireland, by the Act of Union.

10. John Milton.

11. *The Economist*. Wilson saw free trade as 'a great agency for securing peace and charity among men in all parts of the earth'.

12. He was having a cosy game of bridge with three ladies, and Bonar Law was asked to wait until they had finished the rubber. Such frivolity at a time when the country was fighting for its existence was inadvisable. Asquith was replaced by Lloyd George seven months later. But to be fair to Asquith it was the Whitsun Bank Holiday. Lady Tree once asked the prime minister rather archly, 'Mr Asquith, do you take an interest in the war?' He mistakenly assumed she was joking and told her that she had 'a good tho' often disguised sense of humour'.

13. The bandit leader Chang Hsien-chung (or Zhang Xianzhong), more commonly known as 'the Yellow Tiger'.

14. The Capetian dynasty, the thirteen kings descended in direct line from Hugh the Great, Duke of Francia.

* Robin Lane Fox, *Alexander the Great* (Penguin)

1.  He ended a speech during a Westminster by-election with the denunciation, 'What the proprietorship of these papers is aiming at is power, and power without responsibility – the prerogative of the harlot throughout the ages.' Baldwin had indeed lost an immense fortune left to him by his father, and the two press barons Rothermere and Beaverbrook were using this information to oust him from the leadership of the Conservative party. Lady Diana Cooper wrote of the incident, 'I saw the blasé reporters, scribbling semi-consciously, jump out of their skins to a man.'

2.  England under Oliver Cromwell (from John Buchan's biography of Cromwell).

3.  Dick Whittington.

4.  It comes from the tomb of King Mausolus of Caria, at Halicarnassus in Turkey, one of the Seven Wonders of the Ancient World.

5.  Genghis Khan.

6.  The Holy Roman Emperor Frederick II of Hohenstaufen, King of Germany, King of Sicily, King of Jerusalem (1194–1250).

7.  Louis XVI and Marie-Antoinette. Her mother, the Empress Maria Theresa, echoed these fears in a letter: 'You are both so young and the burden which has been placed on your shoulders is very heavy. I am distressed that this should be so.' Marie-Antoinette was eighteen and her husband was seventeen.

8.  Adolf Hitler.

9.  The felicitiously named Thomas Crapper (Wallace Reyburn's biography of Crapper is entitled *Flushed with Pride*). But his name is not a derivation from the vulgar verb/noun with which the use of the WC is associated. *Crappe* is Middle English for 'chaff' and comes from the old Dutch word *krappe*, which probably derives from *krappen* meaning 'to tear off'. Back in 1596 the eccentric Sir John Harington drew up detailed plans for his water closet and a working model was installed at his country house at Kelston in Somerset (to which he had been banished for showing some lewd excerpts from

Ariosto's *Orlando Furioso* to some ladies of the court). It was much admired by his godmother, Elizabeth I, who had one installed at the Palace of Richmond. At one point he amazed everyone by applying for the job of Archbishop of Ireland.

10. Edward VIII.

11. Joan of Arc.

12. Ramsay MacDonald.

13. Sixty-year-old Walter Ralegh. Gondomar demanded retribution after Ralegh's attacks on a Spanish colony during his voyage to find El Dorado along the Orinoco River. James was also invoking an earlier death sentence on Ralegh for plotting against the Crown.

14. The soldier and historian Xenophon, who led an army of 10,000 Greek mercenaries through 1,000 miles of the hostile Persian Empire of Prince Cyrus. 'Thalassa, thalassa! [The sea, the sea!]' cried the exhausted soldiers when they finally sighted the Black Sea.

# ANSWERS TO QUIZ 21

1. 'Good God, that's done it. He's lost us the tarts' vote.'

2. His first cousin, Lady Jane Grey. Edward was suffering from smallpox and galloping consumption. The reluctant Queen is supposed to have declared, 'The crown is not my right and it pleaseth me not.'

3. They flew the Atlantic non-stop for the first time, from Newfoundland to an Irish peat bog at Clifden in 16 hours 12 minutes.

4. Acting as local militias, they were enjoined to suppress vice and encourage virtue (Christmas and the theatre had already been banned). 'Merry England became a silent and melancholy place,' wrote John Buchan in his life of Oliver Cromwell. The experiment was mercifully short.

5. Maximilien Robespierre.

6. The Mongol 'Golden Horde' under Baidar and Qadan. The flower of European chivalry were slaughtered in the carnage. Baidar and Qadan ordered that an ear be cut off every corpse to demonstrate the scale of their victory – nine sacks were sent back to Batu Khan (grandson of Genghis).

7. The Crimean War.

8. Teaching Darwin's theory of evolution. He 'did teach thereof that man has descended from a lower order of animals.' In a case which became known as the 'Monkey Trial', Scopes was found guilty and fined a token $100. A group of pro-Darwinian scientists helped to establish a scholarship at the University of Chicago for Scopes to study geology. When the verdict went before the Tennesseee Supreme Court on appeal, Scopes was too engrossed in his studies to hear it reverse the lower court's decision and cancel the fine.

9. Charles I's unpopular favourite George Villiers, Duke of Buckingham.

10. 'Granted. Recommend "Urinoco".'

11. An Anglo-French Force (including Oliver Cromwell's Ironsides) under Marshall Turenne against the Spanish Army of Flanders under Don John of Austria and the Prince de Condé.

12. Benjamin Disraeli.

13. Viceroy Lord Curzon and Lord Kitchener. Curzon's friends warned him that the new Commander-in-Chief of the Indian Army might be difficult to handle. At the beginning Curzon believed naively that he could manipulate him, writing home, 'He stands aloof and alone, a molten mass of devouring energy and burning ambitions without anybody to control or guide him in the right direction.' Later he described him as 'a caged lion dashing its bruised head against the bars'.

14. The Spanish Inquisition. Juan Antonio Llorente, Secretary of the Inquisition from 1790 to 1792, estimated with some satisfaction in his *History of the Inquisition* that 30,000 people had been put to death in Spain alone.

## ANSWERS TO QUIZ 22

1. William Tyndale. He said to a priest, 'If God spare me my life, ere many years I will cause a boy that driveth the plough shall know more of scriptures than thou doest.' A few years after his death the Great Bible containing his translation of the New Testament was set up in every parish church throughout the land; it later formed the basis of the King James Bible.

2. The House of Lords. 'There are no credentials. They do not even need a medical certificate. They need not be sound either in body or mind. They only require a certificate of birth – just to prove that they are first of the litter. You would not choose a spaniel on these principles,' added Lloyd George.

3. Cardinal Thomas Wolsey. He was impeached and charged with high treason for his failure to persuade the pope to grant the divorce. He died in 1530 *en route* to London.

4. Big Ben. The name is often used of the clock or the clocktower, but it is in fact the name of the clock's great bell. Hall was Commissioner of Works at the time Big Ben was cast in 1858.

5. 'My dear, the "t" is silent, as in Harlow.' Nigel Rees, in his *Guinness Book of Humorous Anecdotes*, says that the English actress Margot Grahame, not Margot Asquith, was responsible for this brilliant one-liner. Grahame always maintained that it was not intended as a put-down and that she did not realize until afterwards what she had said.

6. Bonnie Prince Charlie.

7. The conquistador Hernán Cortés. He claimed untruthfully that the nine ships were unseaworthy, but by this action he committed himself and his men to survival by conquest prior to his conquest of Mexico.

8. An astounded Lord Curzon. Baldwin cattily commented, 'I met Curzon in Downing Street and received the sort of greeting a corpse would give an undertaker.' Curzon commented bitterly that Baldwin was 'not even a public figure. A man of no experience. And of the utmost insignificance. Of the utmost insignificance.'

9. 'You know, this piece of cod passeth all understanding.'

10. The Zinoviev letter. Grigoriy Zinoviev was the demagogic president of the Comintern (or Third International) and the letter exhorted its addressees, the British Communist Party, to 'stir up the masses of the British proletariat' and suggested it would be desirable 'to have cells in all units of the troops'. Believing it to be genuine, Conservative Party Central Office paid £7,500 for it. Its publication in the *Daily Mail* on 25 October, four days before the general election, was a key factor in the defeat of Ramsay MacDonald's Labour government. The forgers, a group of White Russian émigrés led by Alexis Bellegarde and Alexander Gumansky, had hoped to discredit the Bolshevik regime rather than to cause mayhem in British politics. Curiously, no one seems to have asked Zinoviev himself whether the letter was genuine.

11. The conquest of Sicily by Roger, son of the Norman Tancred of Hauteville, and his brother, Robert Guiscard. The rule of Roger and his son Roger II saw the apogee of Sicily as the leading maritime power in the Mediterranean from 1157 to 1166.

12. Maurice de Saxe, one of the 354 (probably a wild exaggeration) illegitimate children of Augustus the Strong of Poland. Saxe was one of the greatest generals of his age, particularly during the War of the Austrian Succession, and like his father he was a legendary lech. His death was probably hastened when he 'interviewed' a troupe of eight actresses.

13. Charles II, after his defeat at the Battle of Worcester.

14. William Howard Russell.

## ANSWERS TO QUIZ 23

1.  Smoking. Napoleon smoked heavily himself.

2.  The British fleet under Sir Edward Hawke against the French off the coast of Brittany, during the Seven Years War. It was one of the most heroic victories in British naval history.

3.  Louis IX (1214–70), the most popular of all the Capetian monarchs. He led the Seventh Crusade and died of the plague in Tunisia. He was canonized by Pope Boniface VIII in 1297.

4.  The Khmer.

5.  'To travel 52 miles in this bad weather, merely to see a man with only the given number of legs, arms, fingers, etc., would, you must admit, be madness...If you can do anything better in the way of pleasing a lady than ordinary men, write directly; if not, adieu, Monsieur le Prince.'

6.  The Spanish Civil War. When the Nationalist General Mola was advancing on Madrid a group of foreign journalists asked him which of his four columns would take the capital. Mola replied that it would be his fifth column of supporters/subversives already in the city.

7.  Antoine-Quentin Fouquier-Tinville who maintained that 'It is the duty of the Convention to abolish all the formalities which impede the march of law.' He therefore worked frenziedly to provide the guillotine with victims – including his friends Robespierre and Danton. He was later guillotined himself, remonstrating that he had only been following orders.

8.  The Dutch fleet under Admiral Michiel de Ruyter at the end of the Second Anglo-Dutch War.

9.  Giuseppe Mazzini.

10. Benjamin Disraeli during the Corn Law repeal crisis.

11. His angry wife, Queen Marie-Thérèse (who had the vapours most of the time), his ex-mistress, Louise de Vallière, and his heavily pregnant current mistress, Athenaïs de Montespan. The group had to

pause for two days at Tournai for Athenaïs to give birth to her third child by the King. Louis's future wife, Mme Scarron (later Mme de Maintenon), was also of the party, in her role as nanny to the second child of Athenaïs and the King.

12. Eighty-four.

13. St Peter. Linus (AD 67–76) was thus the second bishop of Rome or pope.

14. Rehoboam, son of Solomon, from 933 BC. But it was during his reign that the ten northern Hebrew tribes broke away under the leadership of Jeroboam to form the kingdom of Judah.

# ANSWERS TO QUIZ 24

1. David Lloyd George.

2. The Polish-born 'Red' Rosa Luxemburg. She was shot by a Lieutenant Vogel outside the Hotel Eden as she was being arrested during the Spartacus Rising in Berlin on 15 January 1919.

3. The Volstead Act enforced the National Prohibition Act, or 18th Amendment, of 1919. It was duly repealed a little over a week after Roosevelt's inauguration in March 1933. His Republican opponent, Herbert Hoover, had unwisely proclaimed Prohibition 'a great social and economic experiment, noble in motive and far-reaching in purpose' during his election campaign.

4. Margarine. It was the only entry in Napoleon III's competition for a butter substitute for the army. Mège-Mouriés's concoction of suet, skimmed milk and offal was dead white so he called it 'margarine' from the Greek word *margaron*, meaning pearl.

5. General Robert E. Lee, the Confederate Commander-in-Chief.

6. In Spain, between the supporters (predominantly in northern Spain) of the pretender Don Carlos and those of his niece Queen Isabella II after her father, King Ferdinand VII, had set aside the Salic Law to ensure her succession. In the 1830s, 1840s and 1870s Carlists fought unsuccessful civil wars against a liberalized and centralized Spanish monarchy.

7. Lajos Kossuth, who wanted to remove the dead hand of Viennese absolutism. Kossuth became virtual dictator of Hungary after the resignation of the prime minister, Count Lajos Batthyany (and the invasion of Hungary by the Croat Army). 'The next months brought out all of his greatness and his weaknesses: his magnetism and his courage, his intolerance and his lack of realism, his wanton provocation of insuperable difficulties and his genius at overcoming them.'* Kossuth was forced to resign and go into exile after the arrival of the Russian armies.

8. 'Shall a people that 15 years ago was the terror of the world now stoop so low as to tell its inveterate enemy "Take all we have, only give us peace"? My Lords, any state is better than despair; if we must

94

fall, let us fall like men.' The dying Pitt had dragged himself to the House of Lords to make this one last desperate plea.

9. John Wilkes. It was Wilkes's counterblast to Bute's publication *The Briton*. Issue Number 45 of *The North Briton* was particularly defamatory, containing libellous innuendos about Bute's relationship with George III's mother. After its publication Wilkes was arrested, only to be set at liberty by Lord Chief Justice Pratt, who upheld his parliamentary immunity. Wilkes's *Essay on Woman* (a parody of Alexander Pope's *Essay on Man*), published at the same time, was deemed extremely obscene and landed him in the Tower of London for four days. Wilkes had intended the work to be seen only by his friends at the Hell-Fire Club, but a copy strayed into enemy hands.

10. Martin Luther at the Diet of Worms. Luther was quite right: Leo X, according to Joseph McCabe, was 'a coarse, frivolous, cynical voluptuary, probably addicted to homosexual vice in the Vatican. He was much given to idleness, pleasure and carnal delights.'

11. Darius II, the Great King of Persia, the last of the Achaemenid dynasty. Alexander wrapped Darius's corpse in his own cloak and promised to accord him a royal burial at Persepolis.

12. Benjamin Disraeli, who was visiting Reschid Ali Pasha, the Turkish Grand Vizier of Albania.

13. Giuseppe Garibaldi.

14. Sir Roger Casement. He was accused of treason for fostering revolution in Germany and was hanged in August 1916.

* *Encyclopaedia Britannica*

## ANSWERS TO QUIZ 25

1. The Dreyfus Affair. Esterhazy's memorandum offering French military secrets to the German government was discovered by a chambermaid at the German Embassy. But Esterhazy was a Catholic officer and an aristocrat to boot – his arrest would have caused enormous political embarrassment. So Dreyfus was fingered instead.

2. Napoleon III's.

3. 'If a traveller was informed that such a man was Leader of the House of Commons, he might begin to comprehend how the Egyptians worshipped an insect.'

4. The Duke of Monmouth (Charles II's illegitimate son) and Anthony Ashley Cooper, the Earl of Shaftesbury. Shaftesbury had conspired with the Protestant Monmouth to exclude the Catholic James II from the throne. Charles II had asked Dryden to write the poem.

5. *The King and I.* Mongkut of Siam had been a monk for twenty-six years before he succeeded his half-brother to the throne, but made up for lost time by acquiring thirty wives within four months. He fathered eighty-two children during his seventeen-year reign. But he found the time to become one of Asia's most distinguished statesmen, who 'steered his country through the conflicting pressures and territorial ambitions of France and England and set the course that preserved the independence of his country . . . He towered morally over his contemporaries, not only in Siam, but throughout south-east Asia.'* He was tolerant, intellectually curious and devoid of the capricious cruelties imputed to him by the governess Anna Leonowens and the later embellishments of Margaret Landon, who wrote the bestseller *Anna and the King of Siam.*

6. Fragments of a jaw and huge skull dug up from a chalk quarry near Maastricht in 1780. It was the first 'dinosaur' skeleton to be found (actually *Mosasaurus*, a gigantic marine lizard).

7. A Mesopotamian temple tower.

8. Buddha died in 483 BC and Confucius in c. 479 BC.

9. Winston Churchill.

10. William Gladstone, who championed particularly the cause of the lawyer Carlo Poerio.

11. The Russo-Japanese War of 1904–5, which culminated in the annihilation of the Russian fleet at the Battle of Tsushima.

12. The Briand–Kellogg Pact, which 'pledged to eschew the use of arms' to resolve conflict. It was eventually signed by 65 nations (including Japan and Germany).

13. The Battle of Wounded Knee on 29 December 1890, when 249 Sioux people (mainly women and children) were massacred indiscriminately at the Pine Ridge Indian Reservation in South Dakota.

14. The 1918 Armistice.

* Abbot Low Moffat, *Mongkut the King of Siam* (Cornell)

# ANSWERS TO QUIZ 26

1.  To celebrate the birthday of the famous *grande horizontale* Caroline 'La Belle' Otero. They were all her past or present lovers. At a later birthday they could have been joined by the Shah of Persia, the Khedive of Egypt, King Alfonso XIII of Spain, Kaiser Wilhelm II and Aristide Briand.

2.  The Battle of Verdun.

3.  Sir Frank Whittle.

4.  Apollonius the 'Great Geometer'. His treatise *Conics* (conic sections) is one of the greatest scientific works of the ancient world.

5.  Mahatma Gandhi. He denounced the tax as 'a nefarious monopoly' and upon his arrival on the beach at Dandi picked up some grains of salt left by the waves and held them up in his first act of defiance against the British Raj. Thousands and thousands of villagers along India's long sea coast took their cue from the Mahatma and collected salt in a mass peaceful protest. Salt is an essential commodity in the tropical heat of India.

6.  'I speak Spanish to God, Italian to women, French to men and German to my horse.'

7.  Mustafa Kemal Atatürk, from 29 October 1923.

8.  Denmark, Sweden and Norway, under the leadership of Queen Margaret of Norway. Her great-nephew Duke Erik VII of Pomerania was crowned King of Scandinavia.

9.  Bishop Latimer, while he and Bishop Ridley were being burnt at the stake during the Marian Persecutions.

10. Cyrus the Great (550–29 BC), who overthrew the Median king Astyages, conquered Lydia and Babylonia and extended his empire into Asia.

11. Elizabeth of Bohemia, wife of Frederick, Elector of the Palatinate, who was offered the crown of Bohemia by the Protestant establishment in defiance of Holy Roman Emperor Ferdinand II in 1619.

## 26

They ruled for just one winter before the Bohemian army was defeated at the Battle of White Mountain (just outside Prague) by Imperial forces in the first major engagement of the Thirty Years War. The couple fled into exile in Holland. The beautiful Elizabeth, daughter of James I of England, was also known as 'the Queen of Hearts'.

12. Ramsay MacDonald.

13. The enormously grand Lord Curzon, who was the son of a mere baron, the fourth Baron Scarsdale.

14. Rasputin. They poisoned him, shot him and threw him into the River Neva just for good measure.

# ANSWERS TO QUIZ 27

1. She was reminiscing about the day she had made love to Baron Lepic in a hot-air balloon 200 feet over the River Aude in France.

2. Daniele Manin, who declared himself President of the new Independent Venetian Republic. The struggle was lost with the Austrian victory at the Battle of Novara, but Manin continued his heroic defence of Venice until typhoid, bombardment and starvation forced his surrender to the Austrians in August 1849. Manin died in exile but was given a state funeral in liberated Venice in 1868.

3. The National Socialists or Nazi Party gained 107 seats, to become the second largest party in the Reichstag.

4. The First Sea Lord, Prince Louis of Battenberg, and the distinguished army reformer Lord Chancellor Haldane. Haldane's chance remark at a dinner party that Germany was his 'spiritual home' – referring to his study of philosophy at Göttingen University forty years earlier – was completely misinterpreted.

5. The Great Trek. They led the Boer Voortrekkers out of British rule north across the Orange River into the uncolonized lands of northern Natal.

6. Captain James Cook.

7. 'You are forgetting the post-chaise.' Ironically, a year later Charles did need his post-chaise when he was forced to abdicate (in 1830).

8. The Kuomintang or Nationalist Party.

9. Mayonnaise. The only ingredients he could find on board were oil, vinegar and eggs.

10. The Russian Constitution. Thomas Carlyle, in his *History of the French Revolution*, described France as 'a long despotism tempered by epigrams'.

11. The calculating and sinister Choderlos de Laclos, author of *Les Liaisons dangereuses*. Laclos was a retired artillery officer of Spanish origin. It was during an uneventful posting at Aix, near La Rochelle,

that he wrote *Les Liaisons* in 1779. At the Palais Royal he immediately commenced a energetic and rigorous programme of anti-Court pamphlet-writing. 'Unknown, unscrupulous, and unafraid of the greatest designs, he preferred to work behind the mask of his royal master. He could listen to the applause and the shouting and feel the thrill of power without every facing the fickleness of the crowd.'\*
Henceforth he became the soul of the Orleanist Party culminating in his unsuccessful attempt to get the Duke elected Regent after Louis XVI's disastrous escape attempt to Varennes. Perhaps rather surprisingly, the cynical Laclos became an uxorious husband and a doting father. In 1800 he rejoined the army and fought under Marshal Marmont, reaching the rank of general.

12. General Francisco Franco.

13. Abraham Lincoln (also attributed to Phineas T. Barnum).

14. The Crimean War.

---

\* Evarts S. Scudder, *Prince of the Blood* (Collins)

## ANSWERS TO QUIZ 28

1.  Benjamin Disraeli.

2.  The first effective process for quick-freezing food.

3.  Napoleon. Ney accepted the inevitability of the Bourbon restoration and urged Napoleon to abdicate, but returned to the Emperor's side after his escape from Elba and fought with him at Waterloo. Ney was later executed on a charge of treason.

4.  Lord Byron.

5.  Thomas Cranmer, after facilitating Henry VIII's divorce from Catherine of Aragon and his marriage to Anne Boleyn. '. . . his liturgy, the Book of Common Prayer, shaped the English mind for four centuries, united Englishmen as nothing else did, and reached a world Shakespeare never touched.'* He was burnt at the stake during the Marian Persecutions.

6.  Macbeth. Although Macbeth almost certainly had a hand in the killing of the unpopular and tyrannical King Duncan after the Battle of Burghead, he could not have murdered Banquo and Macduff's family because there is no contemporary evidence of their existence. They were inventions of the sixteenth-century historian Hector Boece, a fellow student of Erasmus and first principal of Aberdeen University. William Shakespeare turned to Raphael Holinshed for his background material, as Holinshed had turned to Boece and the earlier historians John of Fordun and Andrew of Wyntoun. In reality, Macbeth's seventeen-year rule was an oasis of peace and prosperity in Scotland.

7.  'You lose.'

8.  King Louis-Philippe and Queen Marie-Amélie of France, after his abdication in 1848.

9.  He bribed the skipper of the ship carrying his opponent's supporters (from London) to land them in Norway instead of at Berwick. To no avail: he polled only 192 votes at a cost of £4,000. He was eventually returned as MP for Aylesbury after an election campaign which cost £7,000 in bribes to voters.

10. Catherine the Great of Russia.

11. The Byzantine Empress Theodora. The description was coloured by Procopius's hatred of Theodora and her husband, the Emperor Justinian, and is one of the nastiest character assassinations in history.

12. Sébastien le Prestre de Vauban, Marshal of France, who revolutionized siege warfare and provided France with a complete system of aesthetic-ally pleasing fortifications along her eastern frontiers. He also invented the socket bayonet.

13. Michael Collins, a leader of the Irish Republican Army and a member of Sinn Fein. Collins was assassinated in a road ambush by extremists the following year. His co-signatory, Lord Chancellor F. E. Smith (Lord Birkenhead), was equally nervous: 'I may have signed my political death warrant tonight.'

14. The Boer War. The Transvaal and the Orange Free State accepted British sovereignty.

* John Vincent, *An Intelligent Person's Guide To History* (Duckworth)

# ANSWERS TO QUIZ 29

1. Charles de Batz-Castelmore, Sieur d'Artagnan. Alexandre Dumas based his book *The Three Musketeers* on Gatien de Courtilz's *Memoirs of M. d'Artagnan*. The real d'Artagnan died at the Siege of Maastricht in 1673. A month before his arrest Fouquet had made the fatal mistake of inviting Louis (and 6,000 others) to a house-warming at his newly built château at Vaux-le-Vicomte. The king was outraged by its incredible opulence and grandeur, knowing that it had been paid for by public money. But it did give him lots of ideas and inspiration for Versailles. Fouquet narrowly escaped a death sentence, and died in prison nineteen years later.

2. He found himself crouching between the Bishop of Chester and his wife.

3. Doges of Venice (Ipato 726–37, Manin 1789–97).

4. King Louis-Philippe. Other aristocratic scandals in 1847 included the Comte de Bresson, who cut his throat, Prince d'Eckmuhl's stabbing his mistress, and Comte Mortiser's attempted murder of his children. A sustained campaign of press vilification against the well-meaning king did not help matters. He was also mercilessly caricatured by Charles Philipon and Honoré Daumier.

5. Giuseppe Garibaldi. The heavily pregnant Anita died in his arms in the marshes of Ravenna after their epic retreat from Rome in 1849.

6. The bazooka.

7. 'An honest man sent to lie abroad for the good of his country.' Sir Henry was an ambassador in the employ of James I, who was not amused by the jest.

8. Between Stockton and Darlington. It was opened on 27 September 1825 with George Stephenson's 'Locomotion engine' as the star attraction.

9. General Charles Gordon.

10. Benjamin Disraeli. But 'in wrecking Peel's career Bentinck and Disraeli came very near to wrecking his and their party too. Between 1846 and 1886 there was to be only one Conservative administration with a clear majority behind it in the House of Commons. All the rest were short-lived minority governments existing only because of their opponents' dissensions.'*

11. 'How can they tell?' Coolidge's nickname was 'Silent Cal'.

12. He had refused to take the oath of allegiance when he entered parliament. The 1888 Act permitted MPs to make an affirmation of allegiance.

13. Winston Churchill.

14. Trade Unions.

* Robert Blake, *Disraeli* (Methuen)

# ANSWERS TO QUIZ 30

1. Abraham Lincoln's Gettysburg Address – considered by many to be the greatest speech ever written. The *Chicago Times* also felt that all Americans should be embarrassed by Lincoln's 'dish-watery utterances'.

2. The Greek Revolt against the Ottoman Empire. After General Alexander Ypsilanti raised an abortive rebellion in Bessarabia and Moldavia in March 1821, Georgios Germanos, Metropolitan Bishop of Patros, raised the flag of revolution in the northern Morea (Peloponnese) at the monastery of Agia Lavra near Kalavrita. Soon the whole of Morea took up arms, killing 15,000 Turks.

3. The French physicist Jean Bernard Léon Foucault.

4. The American Civil War. When Abraham Lincoln signalled his intention to re-supply the South Carolina fort, General Pierre Beauregard ordered his Confederate troops to open fire and forced the Union troops to evacuate the fort.

5. Eight.

6. 'Don't talk to me about naval tradition. It's nothing more than rum, sodomy and the lash.'

7. 'Muck-raker'. They were all involved in exposing various scandals in business and public life during the early years of this century. Sinclair won a Pulitzer Prize in 1943 for his novel *The Jungle*, an exposé of unhygienic conditions in the meat-packing industry. The word was coined by an angry Theodore Roosevelt during a speech in 1906. He in turn had borrowed the word from the name of a character in John Bunyan's *Pilgrim's Progress*, 'the Man with the Muckrake'. Roosevelt later added, 'The men with the muck-rakes are often indispensable to the well-being of the society; but only if they know when to stop raking the muck.'

8. The Weimar Republic in Germany, which struggled to cope with chronic instability, inflation and unemployment, not to mention the war reparations imposed upon it at the Treaty of Versailles.

9. 'The aeroplane stays up because it doesn't have time to fall down.'

10. The Prophet Muhammad. When Muhammad died, the elderly Bakr (573–634) was elected the first Caliph; and it was through his indomitable will that Islam survived the trauma of the Prophet's death. During his brief reign (632–4), Abu Bakr began the expansion of the Caliphate Empire over Persia, Iraq and the Middle East. He also began the compilation of the Quran.

11. The English philosopher John Locke (1632–1704), founder of British empiricism, who in his *Essay Concerning Human Understanding* and his two *Treatises of Government* refuted the theory of the divine right of kings.

12. Fifty of Rome's most beautiful and scantily clad prostitutes. Cesare Borgia had arranged the entertainment in the Vatican for his father, Pope Alexander VI, and his sister Lucrezia. It became known as 'The Joust of the Whores' and was witnessed and carefully recorded by a very shocked German chaplain called Johann Buchard.

13. Leon Trotsky.

14. The fleet of the Holy League (which comprised Spain, the dominions of Pope Pius V and the Republic of Venice), under the command of Don John of Austria, against the massive Turkish fleet under Ali Pasha; the Turks were attempting to take the island of Cyprus from Venice. The Holy League's victory 'lifted the pall of terror which had shrouded eastern and central Europe since 1453' at a cost of 33,000 lives – the bloodiest naval battle of all time.

## ANSWERS TO QUIZ 31

1. The Empress Eugénie of France.

2. The Battle of Navarino, fought during the Greek War of Independence. On 20 October 1827, in the Peloponnesian harbour of Navarino, a combined British, French and Russian fleet under Admiral Codrington defeated the Egyptian–Turkish fleet under Ibrahim Pasha.

3. Honoré-Gabriel, Comte de Mirabeau. The reckless youth was imprisoned for abducting Sophie, Marquise de Monnier. He was released on condition he went back to his wife – but he didn't. Mirabeau père lightened the burden of his own marriage, which he described as 'one long renal colic', by shutting his wife up in a convent.

4. Prime Minister Sir Robert Peel received a letter reporting the first appearance of potato blight in Britain.

5. 'A typical triumph of modern science to find the only part of Randolph that was not malignant and remove it.'

6. He promised to give up alcohol. When the announcement from Windsor was printed in the stiff *Court Circular*, it was immediately followed by the statement, 'The Earl of Rosebery and the Hon A. J. Balfour have left the Castle.'

7. Field Marshal Lord Roberts of Kandahar replaced General Sir Redvers Buller after Buller's disastrous defeat at Colenso.

8. Rupert Brooke.

9. 'One of the countless drawbacks of being in Congress is that I am compelled to receive impertinent letters from a jackass like you in which you say I promised to have the Sierra Madre mountains re-forested and I have been in Congress two months and I haven't done it. Will you take two running jumps and go to hell.'

10. Sir Roger Casement. His reports on the Congo in 1914 and Peru in 1912 earned him a knighthood.

11. The *Mary Celeste* (yes, that is her correct name, even though many people call her the *Marie Celeste*).

12. It was the first document to be written in the English language.

13. His faithful squire, the troubadour Blondel. In a rather bizarre incident in 1991, an Austrian driving instructor called Eric and his brother took to the road in chain mail and on horseback and rode to London to deliver a letter to Buckingham Palace apologizing for the kidnap of Richard eight hundred years earlier. Eric had seen a film about the Lionheart when he was nine and had become obsessed with the idea of an apology.

14. Greece. Otto of Bavaria eventually got the job, but his rule was autocratic and unpopular. Thirty years later he was deposed and the Greek crown was offered to Lord Stanley (later Lord Derby). His friend Benjamin Disraeli commented on his anticipated refusal, 'It is a dazzling adventure for the House of Stanley, but they are not an imaginative race, and, I fancy, they will prefer Knowsley to the Parthenon and Lancashire to the Attic plain.'

## ANSWERS TO QUIZ 32

1.  Most of the Arab world, into French and British mandates or spheres of influence. Mesopotamia and Iraq went to the British, and Syria and Cilicia to the French. Georges Picot was French High Commissioner in Syria; Sir Mark Sykes was a diplomatist and MP.

2.  Giuseppe Garibaldi.

3.  In a slightly menacing way it established the possibility that the Holy Roman Emperor Leopold and Frederick William of Prussia might unite to restore Louis XVI.

4.  Stanley Baldwin.

5.  Esperanto, now spoken fluently by eight million people.

6.  The American Civil War, in March 1862, in Virginia.

7.  President Georges Clemenceau.

8.  Probably not Nicholas II. The line was broken after the reign of Peter III. Peter was Catherine the Great's husband, but her lover Sergei Saltikov was almost certainly the father of her son Tsar Paul I.

9.  Camille Desmoulins.

10. Coffee. In his diary for 1637, John Evelyn wrote, 'There came in my time to the College [Balliol College, Oxford] one Nathaniel Conopius [*sic*], out of Greece, from Cyrill, the patriarch of Constantinople, who, returning many years after, was made (as I understand) Bishop of Smyrna. He was the first I ever saw drink coffee; which custom came not into England till thirty years after.'* In fact, 'twenty years after' would have been more accurate. Coffee-drinking became common, and coffee houses were set up, in England during the 1650s.

11. The 93rd Sutherland Highlanders. In one of his dispatches, *Times* correspondent William Howard Russell referred to the 'dash on towards that thin red line, tipped with steel'.

12. 'It is not for me, your honour, to attempt to fathom the inscrutable workings of Providence.'

13. Cyrus the Great, King of Persia.

14. In a hot-air balloon.

**32**

* *The Diary of John Evelyn*, edited by William Bray (J. M. Dent: Everyman's Library)

## ANSWERS TO QUIZ 33

1. The area in Ireland where English law was not acknowledged or respected. In the mid-fourteenth century this consisted of Dublin, Louth, Meath, Kilkenny, Trim and Kildare, but thereafter it was to shrink slowly until the Tudors reasserted English rule.

2. The Assyrian.

3. One hundred and sixteen years.

4. His was the shortest reign of any European monarch. When he and his father were assassinated in Lisbon in 1908, the young Crown Prince survived his father by only about twenty minutes. A possible contender for the record is the even shorter reign of Louis XIX, the last Dauphin of France and the son of Charles X, who abdicated in July 1830 in favour of his grandson Henri (V), Duc de Bordeaux. But in the few minutes between his father's signature of abdication and his own signature of abdication Louis was indisputedly a reigning monarch. Their abdications in favour of the Duc de Bordeaux came to nothing: the people did not want him. They settled for Louis-Philippe, Duc d'Orléans.

5. Robert Catesby, not Guy Fawkes. Catesby was shot while resisting arrest.

6. Ulysses S. Grant.

7. Lord Aberdeen.

8. Admiral 'Jacky' Fisher.

9. Senator David Rice Aitchison. He took office for one day only *pro tempore* in place of Zachary 'Old Rough-and-Ready' Taylor, who had refused to take the presidential oath on a Sunday. He insisted it should be recorded on his memorial stone in Missouri which reads: 'David Rice Aitchison, 1807–1886. President of the U.S. one day'.

10. Victor Hugo. From the moment of his arrival he hardly drew breath, issuing endless verbose proclamations and always wearing a military kepi. 'Let the streets of the town devour the enemy, let windows burst

112

open with with fury . . . let the tombs cry out . . . despotism has attacked liberty' and so on. 'Lyons, take thy gun; Bordeaux, take thy carbine; Rouen, draw thy sword; and thou, Marseille, sing thy song, and become terrible!' cried the patriotic septuagenarian.

11. The Gascons ambushed and slaughtered the rearguard of Charlemagne's army during the retreat from his Spanish campaign. The engagement was made famous by the medieval ballad *La Chanson de Roland*.

12. General Miguel Primo de Rivera.

13. The Penny Post.

14. Erich von Ludendorff.

# ANSWERS TO QUIZ 34

1.  Julius Caesar.

2.  The Franco-Prussian War (1870–71). The Spanish crown had been offered to the Prussian Prince Leopold of Hohenzollern. Although he refused it, the French government demanded from Kaiser Wilhelm a promise that there would be no subsequent claims. This led to the infamous Ems telegram which precipitated the war.

3.  'Even God Almighty only had ten.' Georges Clemenceau once complained in a similar vein, 'How can I talk to a fellow who thinks himself the first man in two thousand years to know anything about peace on earth?'

4.  George V.

5.  James II.

6.  James Hepburn, Earl of Bothwell, the third husband of Mary Queen of Scots.

7.  'To which of you charming ladies am I indebted for the delightful incident in the tunnel?'

8.  John Graham of Claverhouse, Lord Dundee. He led the uprising in support of James II and was killed at the Pass of Killiecrankie in 1689.

9.  John Bright.

10. Her detailed records revealed that she seduced 439 monks. She claimed to have had 4,959 lovers in twenty years.

11. Louis Philippe, Duc d'Orléans, the king's cousin. He could have abstained from voting, but he didn't. Louis Philippe himself went to the guillotine ten months after the king.

12. The naval mutiny at the Nore in 1797. John Masefield described conditions on eighteenth-century warships as 'brutalising, cruel and horrible'. Worse still, the seamen were virtual prisoners for two or three years at a stretch (in one case, nine years), since men who were

allowed ashore rarely returned. An ordinary seaman was paid 19 shillings a month, but after deductions would be lucky to see more than 10s of that. This paltry pay was often years and years in arrears. At the time of the Nore Mutiny, there were ships of the line whose men had not been paid for eight, ten, twelve and even fifteen years.

13. The Battle of Towton, in north Yorkshire, in 1461 during the Wars of the Roses. The total loss of life is believed to have been between 28,000 and 35,000.

14. The 703-ton *Sirius* sailed from Cork on 4 April, arriving in New York on 23 April 1838. Brunel's *Great Western* was hot on her heels, arriving only a few hours later.

## ANSWERS TO QUIZ 35

1.  The recovery by the Spanish of the Iberian peninsula from the Moors.

2.  Prince Edward ('Eddy'), Duke of Clarence, eldest son of Edward VII. But no proof has every been uncovered to substantiate this. The listless youth died of pneumonia.

3.  Fyodor Dostoyevsky. His death sentence was commuted at the very last moment and he served four years' hard labour in Siberia.

4.  Her husband, Herbert H. Asquith.

5.  Principally because of the Quran's ban on alcohol. Vladimir knew he would have difficulty in persuading his people to give up their vodka during the long, bitterly cold Russian winters. His emissaries returned from their visit to the opulent Constantinople with glowing reports: 'They did not know whether they were in heaven or on earth. They only knew that God dwells there among men. They could never forget that beauty.' So Orthodox Christianity was adopted speedily and the population of Kiev was baptised en masse in the River Dnieper. Although Vladimir's decision was pragmatic, his own conversion was sincere.

6.  Thomas Jefferson in a letter to Baron Humboldt.

7.  They threw themselves off the cliffs at Masada, Israel.

8.  Napoleon.

9.  They were Afrikaners confined in the British concentration camps during the Boer War.

10. In 1679 to members of the faction which opposed the accession of the Roman Catholic James, Duke of York, later James II.

11. Venice.

12. 'If I once started doing that, I would have to fight every gentleman in town.'

13. 'Gerrymander', from his attempt to rig electoral boundaries in Massachusetts so as to benefit the Republican Party during the 1813 election. 'Mander' was added because one of the new electoral districts was shaped like a salamander.

14. The Habsburg Emperor Ferdinand, who was epilectic, rickety and feeble-minded. Lord Palmerston dismissed him as 'a perfect nullity, next thing to an idiot'.

## ANSWERS TO QUIZ 36

1. They both had a hand in designing the bra. There is no truth in the rumour about Otto Titslinger.

2. Nathan M. Rothschild.

3. Admiral Horatio Nelson.

4. The young Richard Cromwell (nicknamed 'Tumbledown Dick'), son of Oliver. He was finally allowed to flee to the Continent on the eve of the Restoration to live under an assumed name, leaving his wife, Dorothy, to bring up their three young daughters alone. Richard returned to England in 1680 after his wife's death.

5. Arthur Balfour. In his declaration he had proclaimed that 'nothing shall be done to prejudice the civil and religious rights of other non-Jewish communities in Palestine.' As the Arabs formed 90 per cent of the population of the country, J. M. N. Jeffries asserted that to refer to them as the 'non-Jewish communities' was tantamount to 'calling the grass of the countryside the non-dandelion portion of the pastures'.

6. Edward Cardwell. He abolished flogging as a military punishment and the purchase of military commissions which had enabled generations of rich young men to buy commands for which they were unfitted. The six-week-long campaign which culminated in Sir Garnet Wolseley's victory over 'Urabi Pasha at Tel el-Kebir (which resulted effectively in the British conquest of Egypt) demonstrated the value of his reforms.

7. Lord Halifax (formerly Lord Irwin).

8. Holy Roman Emperor Charles V. His wars with Süleyman the Magnificent's Ottoman Empire and Francis I's France (known as the Italian Wars) distracted him from halting the inexorable rise of Protestantism/Lutheranism in his northern lands. He retired, exhausted, to a monastery at Yuste in Spain.

9. The Great Crash. On 5 September 1929 he predicted that 'Sooner or later a crash is coming, and it may be terrific . . . Factories will shut down . . . men will be thrown out of work . . . the vicious circle will

get in full swing and the result will be a serious business depression.' It began on 24 September, reaching its nadir on 29 October.

10. They raised the Siege of Lucknow, during the Indian Mutiny.

11. Incitatus was his horse.

12. Three thousand Zulu warriors under King Dingane by the Boer Voortrekkers under Piet Retief and Andries Pretorius.

13. Ramsay MacDonald died of heart failure during a cruise to South America on the *Reina del Pacífico*.

14. Napoleon, who apparently had twenty-two of the thirty recognized symptoms of arsenical poisoning. In the 1950s a Swedish dentist called Sten Forshufvud did a lot of research into the case and concluded that it was extremely unlikely that Napoleon could have absorbed into his body enough arsenic to kill him: someone must therefore have helped things along a little. Forshufvud believed the most likely candidate was the Comte d'Artois, the future Charles X of France, who hated anything to do with the Revolution or Napoleon.

## ANSWERS TO QUIZ 37

1. George Stephenson.

2. The Trojan War, c. 1260 BC. Recent archaeological findings have uncovered a much larger city than anything found in earlier excavations, with palaces, cemeteries and fortifications. This adds credence to the myth of the great war; historians had been sceptical that such a war could have been fought over a small city.

3. Czechoslovakia.

4. Lord Lansdowne.

5. T. E. Lawrence. George Bernard Shaw and his wife, Charlotte, were close friends of Lawrence, and that fact probably decided Lawrence's choice of name, though he himself denied it. 'Characteristically, he clouded the issue: the new name was the first monosyllable he chanced on in the London telephone book; beginning with S, it came low down on the service duty list, etc. But no author, however reluctant, selects an already famous name by hazard. Bernard Shaw and his secretary Blanche Patch have both confirmed . . . that Lawrence called himself "Shaw after Bernard"'.*

6. 'There are only two ways of getting into the Cabinet. One is to crawl up the staircase of preferment on your belly; the other is to kick them in the teeth. But for God's sake don't mix the two methods.'

7. The nonsense of George Washington and the cherry tree, which comes from Weems's *Life of George Washington: with Curious Anecdotes, Equally Honorable to Himself and Exemplary to His Young Countrymen.*

8. The occupation of Sarajevo in Bosnia-Hercegovina by the Austrian Army. It 'turned out to be in fact a death-sentence for Franz-Josef's successor, for the Empire, and for the Renaissance tradition which, for so long, and with so many setbacks, had inspired all that was best in Europe'.†

9. Richard III. His successors were variously of Welsh, Scottish and German origin.

10. 'Who wouldn't?'

11. The Roman Empire. Women became infertile by drinking wine from lead vessels and water from lead piping. Lead was also used as a sweetening agent. The upper classes virtually died out within a couple of centuries.

12. Paper.

13. The Comte de Mirabeau. His aim during these secret negotiations was to persuade the king and queen to accept a form of constitutional monarchy, but his plans came to nothing because neither the king nor the National Assembly really trusted him.

14. The victory of the Egyptian Mamluks, commanded by Baybars, over the Mongols, commanded by Kitbuga, ended the threat of Mongol domination of the Near East.

* Desmond Stewart, *T. E. Lawrence* (Paladin)
† Edward Crankshaw, *The Fall of the House of Habsburg* (Longman)

## ANSWERS TO QUIZ 38

1. The International Brigade as they marched out of Barcelona on 15 November 1938, towards the end of the Spanish Civil war.

2. William Archibald Spooner. In New College chapel he announced the hymn 'Conquering kings their titles take' as 'Kinquering congs their tykles tate'. One of his students was bewildered to be admonished with the words: 'You have tasted your worm, you have hissed my mystery lectures, and you must leave by the first town drain.'

3. They were the first full-time officers of the Inquisition, which 'in the pope's name, [was] responsible for the most savage and sustained onslaught on human decency in the history of the race'.* As late as 1808, when Napoleon invaded Spain, French soldiers found torture chambers under a Dominican monastery in Madrid. The battle-hardened troops were appalled to find them full of naked prisoners, most of whom had gone insane.

4. Downing Street, after Sir George Downing, diplomat, spy and turncoat. Samuel Pepys called him a 'perfidious rogue'. He was Cromwell's ambassador at The Hague, and later Secretary to the Treasury (from 1670) with responsibility for the Dutch War.

5. Admiral Horatio Nelson. 'Kiss me, Hardy' may have been a mis-hearing of 'It's Kismet, Hardy.'

6. Pocahontas. But did she? Smith had a reputation as a lineshooter, yet he did not mention the incident in the book he wrote shortly after the incident had occurred. It was probably a form of tribal ritual of iniation into the Powhatan tribe.

7. 'L'Éprouveuse'. It was rumoured that she volunteered to test the sexual abilities of Catherine's potential young lovers.

8. Time became, retrospectively, immemorial. In 1275 the Statute of Westminster set a limit to the time of legal memory; precedents and customs before that time could not be cited.

9. Ivan the Terrible. *Grozny* really means 'awe-inspiring'.

10. Madame de Montespan. She had attempted to poison her young rival, Mademoiselle de Fontanges.

11. 'Electricity', from the Greek word *elektron* meaning 'amber'. The Greek philosopher Thales first identified static electricity when he noticed that the amber decorations on spinning-wheels attracted threads and feathers.

12. Nero. A Sporus of a much later age was Lord John Hervey (1696–1743), the most notorious homosexual of his day, who was nicknamed Sporus, with some venom, by the poet Alexander Pope. William Pulteney, Earl of Bath, described him as 'such a nice composition of the two sexes, that it is difficult to distinguish which is the most predominant'. Also known as 'Lord Fanny', a 'powder-puff' and 'Lord Fainlove', Hervey fathered eight children and fought a number of duels.

13. Mohandas K. Gandhi.

14. The papacy during the tenth century, when it was dominated by Theodora, wife of Theophylact, and her notorious daughter Maroiza, Senatrix of Rome. Between them they created and destroyed no fewer than eight popes.

* Peter de Rosa, *Vicars of Christ: The Dark Side of the Papacy* (Corgi Books)

1.  The purchase of Alaska from Russia for $7 million in 1867, promoted by Secretary of the Interior William Seward. The government paid two cents an acre. The 'utterly useless' new territory was also laughingly referred to as 'Seward's Icebox', 'Polararia' and 'Icebergia'.

2.  Miguel Cervantes. He was captured and enslaved by the Barbary pirates and four years later spent five years as a prisoner in Algiers.

3.  Lady Godiva.

4.  Sir Robert Peel.

5.  Muhammad Ali.

6.  Dr Samuel S. Mudd, who treated Wilkes-Booth for a broken leg sustained during his escape. When he realized who his patient was the good doctor told the authorities, but he was immediately charged as a co-conspirator and sentenced to life imprisonment on Shark Island. He was pardoned after he had risked his own life treating prisoners with yellow fever. This is not the origin of the expression 'My name is mud'.

7.  He found 'the Holy Arab city of Damascus was a city of the dead. The narrow streets which he paced after dark were deserted and silent. Not a sound came the high shuttered walls of the houses.'* In stark contrast he one night observed a bar full of Italian workers singing and dancing with their wives and girlfriends. From that moment Atatürk drank freely and openly. The incident made him determined that the future Turkey would be a secular state.

8.  The progeny of Elizabeth Harley, wife of Edward Harley, the third Earl of Oxford, who all had different fathers.

9.  The British forces under Robert Clive against the pro-French forces of Siraj ud-Daula, the Nawab of Bengal. Clive, although vastly outnumbered, defeated the Nawab and ensured British supremacy in Bengal.

10. William Gladstone's son Herbert, who prematurely informed the Liberal press of his father's conversion to the idea of Home Rule for Ireland. Hawarden Castle was the Gladstone family home.

11. The ill-fated Gallipoli campaign.

12. An attempt by Sir Edward Grey, Henry H. Asquith and Lord Haldane, the Liberal Imperialists, to remove Henry Campbell-Bannerman from the nominal leadership of the Liberal Party. (The scheme got its name because Grey had a fishing lodge at Relugas in north-east Scotland.) To this end they persuaded Edward VII to offer C-B a peerage. The king said to him coaxingly, 'We are not as young as we were, Sir Henry.' But he was not to be cajoled and when the twenty-stone, domineering Lady Campbell-Bannerman got wind of the plot she scotched it.

13. 'Please remain. You furnish pictures. I will furnish war.' Subsequent wildly exaggerated and jingoistic reporting in the *Journal* and other American newspapers whipped up public opinion against Spain. 'We'll whip the dagos until they howl,' said one New York army volunteer.

14. Serbia's response to the ultimatum issued by Austria after the assassination of Archduke Franz Ferdinand: the Serbs had acceded to almost every Austrian demand. The Kaiser's comments came too late: at noon on that very day, 28 July 1914, Austria declared war on Serbia and the great conflagration began.

* Patrick Kinross, *Atatürk. The Rebirth of a Nation* (Weidenfeld & Nicolson)

## ANSWERS TO QUIZ 40

1. After the scandal of the almost certainly legendary Pope Joan, every new pope had to undergo a sex test by sitting on a marble chair with a hole in the seat (the *sella stercoraria*). The entire ritual appears in various medieval manuscripts.

2. Joseph Fouché, later Duke of Otranto, because of the *mitraillades* (mass executions by cannonade) carried out in Lyon within a few weeks of his arrival there in 1794. Up to sixty prisoners at a time were tied up in line and executed by cannon fire; those unfortunate enough not to be killed instantly were shot with rifles, sabred or bayoneted.

3. Adolf Hitler in *Mein Kampf*. 'The greater the lie, the greater the chance that it will be believed,' he added.

4. The *Daily Telegraph*. Sleigh had to relinquish ownership to his printers after a few months when he could not afford to pay them.

5. Karl Marx.

6. Franklin D. Roosevelt.

7. Otto von Bismarck after his dismissal by Kaiser Wilhelm II in March 1890. The writing was on the wall for Bismarck when, at his accession two years earlier, Wilhelm had commented, 'I shall let the old man snuffle on for six months, then I shall rule myself.' His patience snapped when he arrived at Bismarck's office for a meeting to be told that the old man was still in bed. According to Edward Crankshaw, the dismissal of Bismarck was the wisest decision the Kaiser ever made. 'The trouble was that it was much too late. When the time came, so powerful and all-pervading was the army he had sought to use but which had successfully used him, that there was no escaping its domination.'*

8. Because he had called Lenin's wife, Krupskaya, a 'syphilitic whore' during an acrimonious telephone conversation.

9. Ramsay MacDonald.

10. 'The Cherrybums', because of their tight cherry-pink trousers. 'The brevity of their jackets, the irrationality of their headgear, the incredible tightness of their cherry-coloured pants, altogether defy description; they must be seen to be appreciated,' wrote *The Times*.

11. Sir James Chadwick.

12. Grog. he became known affectionately as 'Old Grog' because he always wore a Grogram coat. It was he who insisted that in the interests of sobriety the rum served to the lower-deck ratings should be diluted.

13. Cardinal Richelieu. Hilaire Belloc in his life of Richelieu describes it as 'among the great military deeds of history'. The starving citizens surrendered after a fourteen-month siege. Two-thirds of the population of 28,000 had perished, and the political power of the Huguenots was destroyed for ever.

14. General Winfield Scott, the veteran soldier and hero of the 1812 Mexican War. Scott was also known by his troops as 'Old Fuss and Feathers' because of his insistence on impeccable uniforms. He lost his fight for the US presidency to Franklin Pierce in 1852.

* Edward Crankshaw, *Bismarck* (Macmillan)

## ANSWERS TO QUIZ 41

1.  President Calvin Coolidge.

2.  Mohandas K. Gandhi.

3.  They were both surprised *in flagrante delicto* and killed by the jealous husbands of their mistresses. 'John had died, violently, but not in battle or by political assassin. The champion of Christendom was an outraged cuckold who had caught his Holy Father in the act and cudgelled him so severely that he died three days afterwards. Or so the gossip ran in Rome.'* Leo VII was 'stricken with paralysis in the act of adultery'.

4.  The democratically elected Popular Front (or Second Republic), a left-wing coalition which came to power in February 1936.

5.  Jean-Paul Marat, Maximilien Robespierre and Georges-Jacques Danton.

6.  Robin Hood.

7.  'That was the only vice he lacked.' Talleyrand gave as good as he got when he quipped, 'One understands why Monsieur Fouché despises his fellow men: he has made so close a study of himself.'

8.  Ali Pasha, sometimes known as 'the Lion of Janina'. The reformist but pragmatic ruler of south Albania once remarked, 'Our speed is limited by the fear of making the boilers burst . . . our metamorphosis must be cautious, gradual, internal and not accomplished by flashes of lightning.'

9.  'This man is mistaken. Turkey is governed by one drunkard.'

10. The Schmalkaldic League founded by the Protestant princes Philip of Hesse and John Frederick of Saxony to oppose Charles V's attempts to reintroduce Catholicism in their lands. This victory was the zenith of Charles's power.

11. Anthony Eden.

12. General Ambrose Everett Burnside, commander of the Army of the Potomac, who was dismissed in January 1863 after his failure at the the Battle of Fredericksburg. He had very distinguished side-whiskers, hence 'sideburns'.

13. 'If I'd just shot an archduke I wouldn't stand around with my feet in concrete.'

14. 'Rien [Nothing].'

* E. R. Chamberlin, *The Bad Popes* (Dorset)

# ANSWERS TO QUIZ 42

1.  The serving prime minister, Ramsay MacDonald.

2.  'We are not amused.' It may not be entirely a coincidence that the great scandal of 'Three-in-a-Bed Dilke' was being widely reported and gossiped about at the time.

3.  The meeting between Karl Marx and Friedrich Engels. Up till then they had only corresponded.

4.  'Go West, Young Man, Go West.' It was taken up by Horace Greeley in the *New York Tribune* in 1865 in a slightly different version: 'Go West, young man and grow with your country.' After the Civil War it was employed to encourage the idea of homesteading among clerks and demobbed soldiers.

5.  Mme Marie Tussaud.

6.  Italy. Its government complained that some of the mandates and colonies promised to it in the 1915 Treaty of London had been ignored.

7.  The first elevator to be equipped with an automatic safety device, designed by Elisha Graves Otis.

8.  'The Lying in State at Westminster'. The Select Committee formally cleared the imperial authorities of any involvement in the raid.

9.  The Unionist General Thomas Hooker, who had a particularly active group of camp-followers. Known as 'Fighting Joe', he succeeded General Burnside as commander of the Army of the Potomac in 1863, but resigned his command six months later after his disastrous defeat at the Battle of Chancellorsville.

10. Bernardo O'Higgins. His Irish father had been the Spanish Viceroy in Peru.

11. Kabul, when the Afghans rose against the British expedition led by Cavagnari. The assassination was avenged when General Sir Frederick Roberts lifted the siege of the British garrison at Kandahar in August the following year.

12. The fully automatic machine-gun. Maxim was knighted by Queen Victoria in 1901.

13. The Nazi Party.

14. The Ghibellines, who were supporters of the German Hohenstaufen dynasty of the Holy Roman Empire. The name derived from the Italian rendition of the Hohenstaufen castle at Waiblingen. Guelph comes from the Italian rendition of the German Welf dynasty – the Brunswick–Lüneburg branch is better known as the House of Hannover.

# ANSWERS TO QUIZ 43

1. Ramsay MacDonald. He became a regular visitor to her Park Lane house, the social centre of the new National Government. Beatrice Webb complained that the affair 'almost amounts to a public scandal'. 'He used to sing the Red Flag,' grumbled members of his own party, 'but now he sings the Londonderry Air.' The friendship was considered particularly scandalous because Lord Londonderry was one of the largest colliery-owners in the country and industrial unrest in the coalfields dominated domestic politics at that time.

2. Between 193 and 268 they were the only emperors not to be assassinated by their own soldiers. Seventeen met their deaths in that way.

3. He sprang to his feet in the Chamber of Deputies, in the face of Napoleon's demand for more troops, and said, 'Have you forgotten where the bones of your sons and brothers whiten? In Africa, on the Tagus, on the Weichsel, in the ice of Russia; two million men have fallen for the sake of one who wished to fight all Europe! It is enough!'

4. Friedrich Engels.

5. '. . . and the rockets' red glare, the bombs bursting in air, gave proof thro' the night that our flag was still there.' In others words, 'The Star-Spangled Banner'.

6. Giuseppe Mazzini.

7. The 'Bonfire of the Vanities' (or 'Burning of the Vanities').

8. Brazil. Cabral followed Vasco da Gama's instructions to sail south-west to avoid the becalmed waters of the Gulf of Guinea. Initially Cabral called the new-found land the Island of the True Cross. It took its modern name from a kind of dyewood, pau-brasil.

9. 'If I had, I should have asked you to my installation. I should have needed a crook.'

10. Peter the Great, who had rented the house during his apprenticeship as a shipbuilder at nearby Deptford. Evelyn's horrified steward reported, 'There is a house full of people and right nasty.'

11. Stonehenge. He later presented it to the nation.

12. Progressive-minded Russian army officers, led by Colonel Paul Pestel, who attempted to overthrow Tsar Nicholas I in December 1825. The attempt was ruthlessly suppressed and the backlash stultified reform for the remainder of Nicholas's reign.

13. Neville Chamberlain, Édouard Daladier of France, Mussolini and Hitler agreed that 13,000 square miles of Czech territory – i.e., the Sudetenland, one-third of Czech territory – should be ceded to Germany.

14. Sinn Fein (meaning 'Ourselves Alone' ).

## ANSWERS TO QUIZ 44

1. Because of the dismemberment of his country at the Munich Agreement.

2. It became an island when the land bridge between it and Europe was flooded.

3. A condom.

4. Indulgences, or pardons, much to the fury of Martin Luther. Gullible Germans could buy a letter of safe-conduct to Paradise for 12 pfennigs. 'As soon as the coin in the coffer rings, a soul from Purgatory springs' was Tetzel's tempting sales patter.

5. Alexander the Great. The knot was a leather thong wound about the shaft of an ancient vehicle in which the mythical King Midas was said to have travelled. According to local legend, the man who undid the knot was destined to rule the world, or at least Asia. The impatient Alexander slashed it in half with his sword.

6. 'From his childhood onwards, this boy will be surrounded by sycophants and flatterers . . . In due course, following the precedent that has already been set, he will be sent on a tour of the world, and probably rumours of a morganatic marriage alliance will follow, and the end of it will be that the country will be called upon to pay the bill.'

7. Tsar Alexander I. Alexander's death in 1825 at the remote town of Taganrog on the Sea of Azov and the knowledge that he had intended to abdicate intensified the rumour. There was almost certainly no truth in it.

8. Benito Mussolini and the four converging columns of his Fascist *squadristi*. The threat was largely symbolic, because Luigi Facta's government had been rendered powerless by King Victor Emmanuel's refusal to declare martial law for fear of precipitating a civil war. Upon Facta's resignation the king reluctantly had to telegram Mussolini in Milan and ask him to form a ministry. Mussolini (who in fact had travelled by train, rather than marching) presented himself to the bewildered king incongruously attired in black shirt, bowler hat

and spats, saying, 'Please excuse my appearance, I come from the battlefield.'

9. The Boer War. Hobson believed the South Africa League was the instrument of 'a small confederacy of international financiers working through a kept press'.

10. 'Madam, you are unlikely to come into contact with either.'

11. Mad Pope Stephen VII dug up his predecessor, Pope Formosus, after nine months and dressed the stinking, putrified corpse in full pontifical robes, placed it on the throne and harangued it for becoming pope under false pretences, pronounced it guilty and threw it into the Tiber, minus the two fingers with which Formosus had given the apostolic blessing. The body was recovered and given a decent burial in St Peter's. But ten years later the equally deranged Sergius III once more exhumed Formosus, condemned him again, beheaded him, removed three more fingers and once again flung him into the Tiber. The corpse seems to have led a charmed death because it was recovered and once more returned to St Peter's for its final – so far – burial.

12. Richard Neville, Earl of Warwick, because of his prominent role in securing the throne for Edward IV.

13. Catherine Howard, Henry VIII's fifth wife. She had affairs with both before her marriage and recklessly renewed her relationship with Culpeper after her marriage. All three paid for their indiscretions with their lives. Catherine and Culpeper were beheaded; the relatively blameless Dereham was disembowelled and castrated while still conscious.

14. The 6,000-mile march of the Chinese Communists from Ruijin in Jiangxi to Yan'an in Shaanxi. In 368 days during 1934–5 the force of 100,000 crossed eighteen mountain ranges and twenty-four rivers arriving at their destination with only 8,000 survivors.

# ANSWERS TO QUIZ 45

1. Henry VI and Edward IV.

2. 'Madam, to which Indians do you refer? Do you mean the second greatest nation on earth, which under benign and munificent British rule has multiplied and prospered exceedingly? Or the unfortunate North American Indians, which under your present administration are almost extinct?'

3. The Dark Ages, the era between the decline of the Roman Empire and the rise of the medieval Christian civilization.

4. Seleukos I Nikator ('the Victorious'), a junior general of Alexander the Great who forged his own empire on the ashes of Alexander's, which had stretched at its zenith from the borders of India to the Aegean Sea.

5. The House of Lords. Arthur Balfour, leader of the Conservative Unionists party in the Upper House, had thrown out Lloyd George's high-tax radical budget (or 'People's budget'). 'The House of Lords is not the watchdog of the Constitution, it is Mr Balfour's Poodle.' The recalcitrant Lords were brought to heel when George V threatened to create a large number of Liberal peers to enable the budget to be passed in the Lords.

6. They were all suspected of being Jack the Ripper. But Prince Albert Victor, Duke of Clarence, had a cast-iron alibi on the night of each murder. In 1996 a television programme put forward yet another candidate, Dr Francis Tumblety, an Irish-American bisexual pornographer from Rochester, New York.

7. 'No, you did.'

8. The Japanese troops guarding the South Manchurian railway attacked the Chinese garrison at Mukden in the north-east of the country on the pretext that the Chinese had planted a bomb on the railway line. In January 1915 the Japanese government had presented its twenty-one demands seeking virtual economic domination of the country. The Chinese government was forced to concede most of them, and Manchuria became known as Manchukuo.

9. Sir Robert (later Lord) Vansittart. As Permanent Under-Secretary of State for Foreign Affairs between 1930 and 1938, he warned the government of Germany's military power, urged immediate re-armament and opposed any appeasement of Hitler.

10. Abraham Lincoln.

11. Sir Rufus Isaacs, in the aftermath of the Marconi insider-dealing scandal. 'As the servant of Elisha, Gehazi had dishonestly obtained a reward from Naaman whom Elisha had cured of leprosy and was punished by being cursed with the disease himself.'*

12. By sheer coincidence the Lords Clifford, Arlington, Buckingham, Ashley and Lauderdale. 'Cabal' is not an acrostic from the names of those lords, as is so often thought, but a Hebrew word.

13. Benedict Arnold, hero of the battles of Quebec and Saratoga. His marriage to a woman with loyalist sympathies, and the fact that he had been passed over for promotion, animated his betrayal. André was captured and hanged. Arnold escaped behind British lines.

14. Arturo Toscanini. He and and his wife were beaten with canes by Fascist thugs, put under house arrest for a month and then allowed to leave the country. His father, Claudio, a follower of Garibaldi, was sentenced to be shot and had to wait while one by one his comrades were placed against the wall and executed. He was reprieved at the last second and imprisoned for three years.

---

* Kenneth Baker, *The Faber Book of English History in Verse* (Faber and Faber)